AUTHOR'S FORI

C000174908

As a writer and seller of books on sequ
requests for details of script collectioι
available at the present day. Section ι ωι ωιι ιωιωιιιω ρ.ω.ιωω
information of this kind suitable for sequence and social dancers
and those preparing for the examinations of the ballroom associations.
For most books the author, publisher, date, number of pages, size,
binding, ISBN number, approximate cost and contents are specified
with details of suppliers. Each script collection and sequence video
described has a full list of the sequence dances included.

Section II of the book brings up-to-date my 'History of Sequence
Dancing and Script List' which deals with dances up to 1994. The
winning sequence dances of the nineties are listed with some general
comments and an index.

Details of the other books bearing my imprint are included in this
volume. It is my intention to keep them all in print at the listed price
for the foreseeable future. They may be obtained (usually by return
of post) by sending a cheque made out to T. A. Whitworth to either:

c/o 60 Dalkeith Road, Harpenden, Herts., AL5 5PW
Tel: 01582 713097 • Fax: 01582 766753

or c/o 42 Newbold Back Lane, Chesterfield, Derbyshire, S40 4HQ
Tel: 01246 278760

ACKNOWLEDGEMENTS

To *Les Barton* for the design and lettering of the front cover.

To *Gordon Lee* for the layout and typesetting of a difficult manuscript.

To many others in the sequence dancing fraternity for advice and
encouragement over the years.

CONTENTS

A SOURCE BOOK FOR SEQUENCE DANCERS

T. A. WHITWORTH
(Chesterfield)

i

First published in September 2000

by

T. A. Whitworth

42 Newbold Back Lane, Chesterfield, S40 4HQ

© T. A. Whitworth

ISBN 0-9501927-8-3

British Library Cataloguing in Publication Data
Whitworth Thomas Alan
A Source Book for Sequence Dancers.
I Title
793.33
ISBN 0-9501927-8-3

Typeset and Printed in Great Britain by:
LEE PRINT SERVICES
Unit 8, Warwick Street Industrial Estate
Storforth Lane, Chesterfield, Derbyshire, S40 2TT
Tel; 01246 237302 • Fax: 01246 272391

ADDRESSES OF SUPPLIERS

Section I.

A DIRECTORY OF RESOURCES.

INTRODUCTION.

This section contains information of general interest to sequence dancers. Suppliers of dance scripts, books and videos are listed with some guidance given on ordering materials by post or through Internet. Contents of books and videos are set out in detail. Priority is given to materials readily available at the present day.

DANCING VENUES.

In the main sequence dancing is a low-cost social activity — a dancing space, recorded music, dance leaders (and some dancers!) are all that are required. Advertisements are seen as expensive and largely unnecessary — recruitment of new members is largely by word-of-mouth. This low profile causes difficulties for beginners and those wishing to dance away from home. Libraries and tourist information centres can be of some help although their lists may be incomplete and not up-to-date. The most effective method is to enquire from someone who dances regularly in the locality. Some publications giving details of sequence dancing sessions are:—

(1) BROCKBANK LANE SEQUENCE SCRIPT DIARY.
This annual production has nearly 30 pages of information on sequence dancing venues in the U.K. and abroad.
Obtainable for £5.95 post free from Brockbank Lane Sequence Script Service, P.O. Box 2341, Weymouth, Dorset, DT4 9YZ.
Tel: 01305 770157. (Ron Lane).

(2) DANCE DIARY.
The 'Tea Dancer' section of this social dance magazine has lists of tea and sequence dance sessions in London and South East England. 4 issues per year for £7.00 post free from 'Dance Diary', 30 The Crescent, Welwyn, Herts., AL6 9JQ. Tel/Fax: 01438 840066. Mobile 07974 258 217. (Eddie Foulds and Olive Elderton).

1

DANCE SCRIPTS

A dance script is a concise set of instructions for performing a particular sequence dance. Dance teachers use scripts to add new dances to their repertoire, ordinary dancers use them to learn, memorise and perform the dances and sort out difficulties with particular steps. Reading dance scripts requires practice since technical terms are used and unnecessary letters and words are eliminated – the language needs to be learnt.

'Learning the Essential Sequence Dances' by T. A. Whitworth (1997) (see page 4) has the early chapters directed to reading dance scripts.

Another way of becoming familiar with the language of dance scripts is to study charts of dancing figures which appear in the more advanced books on ballroom and Latin-American dancing. Dancing figures (see page 15 onwards) are groups of steps with names like reverse turn, whisk and hover cross; they form the basis of the examinations held by various ballroom associations. The figures use the same technical terms and abbreviations found in scripts — the charts can be seen as mini-scripts.

OBTAINING SINGLE SCRIPTS

Small numbers of scripts are readily obtained from:—

(3) NORTHERN DANCE SERVICES (NDS).

18 Commercial Street, Shipley, West Yorks, BD18 3SP.

Tel: 01274 586829. Fax: 01274 585520. (Maureen Pye).

Lists of fun and party dances and dances by year are also available.

Another excellent list of sequence dances is:—

(4) BROCKBANK LANE DANCE SCRIPT LIST.

A set of cards listing all dances issued through the script service in volumes 1 to 49 at £1.70 post free. (See page 3 opposite).

Scripts of all these dances (and many more) may be purchased from Brockbank-Lane at £1.00 each (60p to members) plus postage (currently 1 – 5 scripts 27p, 6 – 10 scripts 41p).

SCRIPTS OF NEW DANCES

There are some 45 new official sequence dances per year. These are prize-winners at the various sequence dance inventive competitions sanctioned by the British Dance Council. (Section II contains details of these dances for the years 1990 to 1999.)

Prizes for new dances are awarded in three categories:—

Old-Time – Old-Time Waltz, Old-Time Tango, Saunter, Blues, Swing, Gavotte, Two Step, Mazurka, Schottische, Glide, Sway, etc.

Modern – Modern Waltz, Modern Tango, Quickstep, Slow Foxtrot, Viennese Waltz.

Latin-American – Rumba, Cha Cha Cha, Samba, Jive, Paso Doble, Bossa Nova, etc.

These new official dances are important since the programmes for accomplished sequence dancers consist mainly of dances from the current year. Attendances at these dancing sessions increase as the new dances appear and there is a great demand for the early supply of scripts by teachers and others. There are two main suppliers of scripts of new dances:—

(5) NORTH STAR PUBLISHERS.

P.O. Box 20, Otley, West Yorks., LS21 2SA

Tel: 01943 462 269. (Derek Arnold).

Subscribers to the service receive the scripts of the new dances as they appear, a dance diary and 'Sequence Dancing World'.

Four different services are available with prices per year depending upon format and speed of delivery. Standard £28.00, Red Star £36.00, De Luxe £45.00 and A4 Service £34.00.

(6) BROCKBANK LANE SEQUENCE SCRIPT SERVICE.

P.O. Box 2341, Weymouth, Dorset, DT4 9YZ. Tel: 01305 770157.

The scripts are supplied on A5 semi-stiff card with man's steps and lady's steps set out in full. The cost of U.K. membership is £27.00 per year. A 'hot off the press' (HOP) service is available for subscribers to obtain immediate delivery of scripts of the new dances by first class post at a cost of 45p + first class postage.

BOOKS OF SCRIPTS WITH A TEACHING ELEMENT

Books on old time sequence dancing often start with an introductory section on theory and technique followed by a collection of scripts with explanatory notes on their performance.

Three teaching manuals with this approach are described below.

(7) LEARNING THE ESSENTIAL SEQUENCE DANCES.

Written and published by Thomas Alan Whitworth. (Dec 1997).

ISBN 0-9501927-7-5. 232 pages, 200 x 130 mm, £8.50 inclusive.

Available from the author at 42 Newbold Back Lane, Chesterfield, S40 4HQ, Tel: 01246 278760, and many other suppliers.

Contents:

SECTION I (CHAPTERS 1 – 4) – The nature of sequence dancing. Aspects of learning. Abbreviations and technical terms. Dance scripts.

SECTION II (CHAPTERS 5 – 11) – Scripts of popular dances with explanatory notes:—

Waltzes:	Sweetheart, Marie, Catherine, Woodside, Emmerdale, Engagement.
Quicksteps:	Mayfair, Broadway, Cameron.
Swings:	Sindy.
Foxtrots:	Harry Lime, Melody, Iris, Glenroy.
Tangos:	Square, Serida, Las Vegas.
Old-Time:	Lilac, Fylde and Pride of Erin Waltzes, Eva Three Step.
Saunters:	Yearning, Together.
Blues:	Lingering, Balmoral, Georgella, Bossa Nova.
Rumbas:	Royal, One, Rosalie.
Cha Cha Chas:	Sally Ann, Wheels.
Jive:	Rock Barn Dance.

(Many other scripts in abbreviated form.)

SECTION III (CHAPTERS 12 – 16) – The lighter side of sequence dancing. Technique and etiquette.

(8) SEQUENCE DANCING.

By Michael Gwynne. Published by A. and C. Black. ISBN 0-7136-2750-6. Second Edition 1985, reprinted 1989. Hard cover. 232 pages. 192 x 125 mm. Some photographs and foot diagrams. £12.99 inclusive.

Out of print but copies still available from many sources.

This book originally appeared as *'Old Time and Sequence Dancing'* in 1950 and has undergone several revisions. It is one of the best books ever written on sequence dancing but now somewhat dated. It has 30 pages dealing with old time theory, a glossary and details of steps for both man and lady for 48 sequence dances. These include many popular dances, the latest being the Tango Solair (1970).

Contents:

(9) SEQUENCE DANCING (KTG).

Produced as part of the Know the Game Series in collaboration with the ISTD. Published originally by E. P. Publishing Co. Ltd. in 1975; Reprinted in 1979 by A. and C. Black.

39 pages, 132 x 202 mm. ISBN 0-7158-0208-9,

Now out of print but available from some suppliers.

Educational Productions Ltd of Wakefield had more than 80 titles in their KTG series covering major sports and pastimes. The dancing books included 'Ballroom Dancing' (1953), 'Old Time Dancing' (1957), 'Latin American Dancing' (1973) and 'Sequence Dancing' (1975). They were produced in collaboration with ISTD and were very popular. They included many photographs and diagrams illustrating the dancing figures.

Contents of Sequence Dancing (1975/1979)

Foreword; Introduction; Music; Positions of Feet; Line of Dance; The Waltz; Pas de Valse; The Waltz in $^2/_4$ and $^6/_8$ time; Veleta; Opening out after Waltz; Boston Two Step; Pas de Basque; Progressive Barn Dance; Lilac Waltz; Royal Empress Tango; Idaho Foxtrot; Mayfair Quickstep; Tango Serida; St. Bernard's Waltz; Abbreviations.

OLDER BOOKS

There are several books, now out of print, that contain scripts and hints on performance of some of the older sequence dances. Copies of these are often to be found in libraries (sometimes in their reserve stock) and in second-hand bookshops. A more effective but expensive way of obtaining an older book is to commission a book search agent who will act on your behalf. The Internet is becoming increasingly useful in locating books of this kind. (See page 43).

Some recommended books by Victor Silvester are *'Sequence Dancing'* (1950), *'Old Time Dancing'* (1949), *'More Old Time Dances'* (1951) and *'The Complete Old Time Dancer'* (1967) – written in collaboration with Walter Whitman. All these were published in hardback by Herbert Jenkins (London).

SCRIPT COLLECTIONS

(10) NORTH STAR PUBLISHERS.

P.O. Box 20, Otley, West Yorks., LS21 2SA.

Tel: 01943 462 269. (Derek Arnold).

North Star Publishers sell the following script collections:—

(10)(a)   Winning Dances of 1995, 1996, 1997, 1998, 1999. 210 x 150 mm. Each volume at £9.95 inclusive.

(10)(b) Winning Dances of 1986/7/8; 1989/90/91; 1992/3/4; 1995/6/7. 210 x 152 mm. Each three-year collection at £19.95 inclusive.

(10)(c) The Top 66 Modern Sequence Favourites.

Editor Derek Arnold. 210 x 150 mm. 72 pages.

ISBN 1-900572-20-6. £15.95 inclusive.

Dances selected by the readers of the 'Sequence Dance World' magazine. (Originally produced in two volumes of 33 dances.)

Contents:

Apple Blossom Waltz	Emmerdale Waltz	Leanne, Tango
April Foxtrot	Engagement Waltz	Linden Swing
Aquarius, Rumba	Evening Foxtrot	Louise, Waltz
Babette, Waltz	Eivona Quickstep	Manhatten Tango
Beguine, Rumba	Glenroy Foxtrot	Mardi Gras Cha Cha
Bella Bossa Nova	Hawaiian Rumba	Marie, Waltz
Bermuda Foxtrot	Honeysuckle Waltz	Mayfair Quickstep
Bluebird Waltz	Idaho Foxtrot	Melody Foxtrot
Broadway Quickstep	Iris Foxtrot	One, Rumba
Cameron Quickstep	Jayde Foxtrot	Quality Quickstep
Caribbean Foxtrot	Jeanine, Waltz	Quando Quickstep
Catherine, Waltz	Jessica Jive	Raynette Foxtrot
Chandella Quickstep	Jetta Jive	Red Rose Saunter
Clinique, Waltz	Karen Foxtrot	Rosalie, Rumba
Commador Cha Cha	Kingfisher Saunter	Rosemount Rumba
Crinoline Waltz	Kontiki Quickstep	Royale, Rumba
Denverdale Waltz	Lancaster Tango	Sally Ann Cha Cha
Ellis Foxtrot	Las Vegas, Tango	Sefton Foxtrot

Sindy Swing	Tempro Foxtrot	Universal Quickstep
Singapore Swing	Torque Tango	Westlyn Waltz
Suhali Tango	Tracy Tango	Woodside Waltz
Telecon Tango	Trelawney Tango	Woodspring Quickstep

(10)(d) THE TOP 66 OLD TIME FAVOURITES.

Editor: Derek Arnold. 68 pages. 210 x 152 mm.

ISBN 1-900572-27-3. £15.95 inclusive.

This volume includes the dances usually associated with medal tests and a selection of old-time favourites. Produced to commemorate the Annual Festival of Old Time Dancing at Queen's Hotel, Leeds — it is a compilation of two books published in 1985.

Contents

Balmoral Blues	Georgella Blues	Premier Two Step
Bambi Blues	Hesitation Waltz	Pride of Erin Waltz
Blue Danube Waltz	Imperial Waltz	Regis Waltz
Boston Two Step	Iris Foxtrot	Revé, Saunter
Breakaway Blues	Killarney Waltz	Rialto Two Step
Britannia Saunter	La Mascotte	Royal Empress Tango
Camay, Waltz	La Rinka	Serida, Tango
Chicago Swing	Latchford Schottische	Sherrie Saunter
Choristers Waltz	Liberty Two Step	Solair, Tango
Chrysanthemum Waltz	Lilac Waltz	Southern Two Step
Classic Gavotte	Lingering Blues	Square Tango
Crinoline Gavotte	Lola Tango	St. Bernard's Waltz
Cuckoo Waltz	Magenta, Tango	Saunter Together
Destiny Waltz	Manhattan Blues	Tango Waltz
Dinky One Step	Marine Four Step	Veleta, The
Donella Tango	Maxina, The	Waverley Two Step
Doris Waltz	Midnight Tango	Wedgewood Blue
Eugene Tango	Military Two Step	White Rose Tango
Eva Three Step	Mississippi Dip	Waltz, Old Time
Fascination, Tango	Moonlight Saunter	Yearning Saunter
Fylde Waltz	Northern Star Waltz	The Holds
Gainsborough Glide	On Leave Foxtrot	Foot Positions

(10)(e) THE BILL AND MAY BOTHAM BOOK OF 48 DANCES.

Editor: Derek Arnold. 1987. 50 pages. 210 x 145 mm.
ISBN 1-900572-28-1. £9.95 inclusive.
Originally published as 'Handbook of Old Time and Sequence Dances' in 1953.

Contents

Introduction	Fantasia Waltz	Picador Tango
Ace of Clubs	Floretta Tango	Pins and Needles
Alistan Waltz	Georgella Blues	Foxtrot
Anniversary Waltz	Georgian Gavotte	Petunia Waltz
Bilmay Two Step	Granada Tango	Queen's Waltz (a)
Birthday Waltz	Ivy One Step	Queen's Waltz (b)
Bohemian Blues	La Rita Saunter	Regal Waltz
Bluebird Waltz	Lingering Blues	Regina Tango
Chicago Maze	Lovers' Saunter	Ricardo Tango
Coronation Saunter	Lunar Waltz	September Saunter
Tango Denise	Manchester Waltz	Swingola Waltz
Dominoe Waltz	Waltz Marie	Tudor Quickstep
Del Rosa Tango	Maryland Foxtrot	Twilight Saunter
Dreamland Waltz	Melody Foxtrot	Twilight Tango
Dream Waltz	Midnight Tango	Westminster Waltz
Elaine Tango	Midnight Waltz	Winfield Quickstep
Epsom Saunter	Naughty Waltz	

(11) 16 BARS OF PURE GOLD (IDTA).

Scripts of 16 popular sequence dances on 10 cards of A5 size (210 x 148 mm) in a folder. £5.00. Obtainable from International Sales, International House, 76 Bennett Road, Brighton, East Sussex, BN2 5JL. Tel: 01273 608583. Fax: 01273 674388.

Contents

The Harry Lime Foxtrot	Sally Ann Cha Cha	Rumba One
Sweetheart Waltz	Balmoral Blues	Sindy Swing
Mayfair Quickstep	Melody Foxtrot	Rumba Royal
Breakaway Blues	Emmerdale Waltz	Tango Serida
Saunter Together	Square Tango	
Ragtime Swing	Bambi Blues	

(12) MODERN AND LATIN SEQUENCE DANCES ISTD.

(1981). 52 pages. 294 x 210 mm. £8.50 inclusive.

Script of 24 dances used for medal tests. Available from ISTD Sales Office, Imperial House, 22/26 Paul Street, London EC2A 4QE. Tel: 020 7377 1577. Fax: 020 7247 6728.

Contents

Caribbean Rumba	Fiesta Cha Cha	Dream Waltz
Marquesa Rumba	Tutti-Frutti Cha Cha	Alpha Waltz
April Samba	Rosita Cha Cha	Idaho Foxtrot
Sapphire Samba	Sally Ann Cha Cha	Grenada Tango
Samba Katrina	Jupiter Jive	Regent Tango
Aggi Samba	Justa Jive	Tracey Quickstep
Paso Madrid	Jubilee Jive	Broadway Quickstep
Paso Deena	Brazilian Samba	Crystal Quickstep

(13) MODERN AND LATIN SEQUENCE DANCES.

88 pages. 240 x 150 mm. £6.50 inclusive. Compiled by the Sequence Advisory Committee of the Official Board of Ballroom Dancing (1981) Scripts of 32 sequence dances for use by teachers preparing candidates for Modern and Latin Sequence tests, competitions and championships. (Now being revised and extended.)

Available from ISTD (address above) or DanceSport International (address opposite).

Contents

Woodside Waltz	Tango Tarquilla	Sapphire Samba
Engagement Waltz	Universal Quickstep	Paso Deena
Waltz Caravelle	Eivona Quickstep	Paso Madrid
Helenbrooke Waltz	Quando Quickstep	Jupiter Jive
Rayen Waltz	Rumba One	Jubilee Jive
Claringo Foxtrot	Rumba Bianco	Justa Jive
Benita Foxtrot	Blue Mosque Rumba	Y. C. Cha Cha
Glenroy Foxtrot	Caribbean Rumba	Rosita Cha Cha
Rosslyn Foxtrot	Marquesa Rumba	Sally Ann Cha Cha
Tango Victoria	Shadow Samba	Tutti-Frutti Cha Cha
Tango El Cid	Samba Katrina	

OLD TIME DANCING

The main old time dances appearing in sequence form are the O/T Waltz, O/T Tango, Saunter, Blues, Swing, Gavotte, Two Step, Mazurka, Schottische, Glide, Sway and Parade.

Some sources of scripts of these old-time sequence dances have already been mentioned. In addition there is a booklet on old-time technique and charts and scripts of championship dances produced by the Official Board (OBBD, BCBD and now BDC). These are intended for dancers studying for dancing qualifications or entering competitions in old-time dancing.

The publications of the Official Board are now distributed by:—

Dance Sport International Ltd. (Hearn and Spencer),

The Courtyard, Aurelia Road, Croydon, Surrey, CR0 3BF.

Tel: 020 8664 8188. Fax: 020 8664 8288.

They may also be obtained from the suppliers listed on page 20.

(14) A GUIDE TO THE THEORY AND TECHNIQUE OF SEQUENCE OLD TIME DANCING.

B.C.B.D. Revised 1995. Reprinted 1997. 24 pages, 210 x 150 mm. £6.00 inclusive from ISTD.

Contents

The five basic foot positions; Parallel foot positions; Alignments; Abbreviations; Holds; Balance, poise and deportment; The Walks; Technical terms; Describing a dance on paper; Musical beat tables; Time signatures; tempo for championship dances; The pas de basque.

(15) SEQUENCE OLD-TIME CHAMPIONSHIP DANCES (BCBD). 20 pages. 210 x 147 mm. £4.95 inclusive.

This booklet contains scripts of dances from the list in the British Council Rule Book which are recognised for Junior Championships.

Contents

Wedgewood Blue	Lilac Waltz	Gainsborough Glide
Gavotte	Waltz Camay	Midnight Tango
Liberty Two Step	Waverley Two Step	Latchford Schottische

(16) CHARTS OF OLD TIME CHAMPIONSHIP DANCES.

Published by the Official Board of Ballroom Dancing.

14 Booklets containing analyses of various old time championship dances. Each 12 pages, 185 x 245 mm. Various dates. Each £2.70 inclusive from ISTD.

Titles of the Booklets

Britannia Saunter; Fylde Waltz; La Mascotte; Lola Tango; Premier Two Step; Royal Empress Tango; Regis Waltz; Saunter Revé; Tango Magenta; Military Two Step; The Waltz; The Veleta; Tango Solair; Boston Two Step.

Excellent scripts with steps for man and lady can be found for most of the remaining championship dances in 'Sequence Dancing' by Michael Gwynne ((11) page 6).

(17) QUESTIONS AND ANSWERS ON THE OLD TIME CHAMPIONSHIP DANCES.

Written and published by Michael Hibberd. (1963).

120 pages, 218 x 140 mm. Unfortunately now out of print.

Contents

Preface; Foreword; Chart; Alignments; Abbreviations; General knowledge; The Old Time Waltz; Veleta; Fylde Waltz; Military Two Step; Imperial Waltz; Premier Two Step; Boston Two Step; Lola Tango; Royal Empress Tango; Gainsborough Glide; Latchford Schottische; La Mascotte; Britannia Saunter; Use of the feet and legs; Personality and grooming.

(18) THE OLD TIME SOCIETY.

Some dancers prefer to devote their time almost exclusively to old time dancing. Their needs are well served by The Society for the Preservation and Appreciation of Old Time Music and Dancing (The Old Time Society). Editor and Secretary: Fred Boast, 31 Dexter Way, Middlewich, Cheshire, CW10 9GH. Tel 01606 834492. Fax 01606 834693. Members receive a newsletter, information about old-time dancing and a list of old-time dance clubs.

FUN AND PARTY DANCES

(19) KEN FULLER'S FUN AND PARTY DANCES.
Published by T. A. Whitworth, 1996. ISBN 0-9501927-5-9. 80 pages.
210 x 148 mm. £6.00 inclusive.
Scripts of 43 dances arranged by Ken Fuller presented with some
light-hearted humour. Available from T. A. Whitworth and many
other suppliers.

Contents

Line and Circle Dances: Stingbeat; Ragmatazz; Sing-a-Long Stroll;
Festival Parade, Samba Circle; Party Line; Social Two Step;
Blackpool Swing; Cracka-Jacka; Social Stroll; Caroliner; Skyliner
Circle Conga; Party Circle.

Partner Progressive dances: Paso España; Macnamara's Two Step;
Klaxon Swing; Cokernut Hop; Boston Barn Dance; Barn Dance
Blues; New Chestnut Tree; Celebration Jive; Island Calypso;
Rainbow Rag; Jingle Jive; Let's Stroll; Good Wishes Waltz; Darktown
Rag; Jive-a-Long; Good Will Saunter; Party Mix; Swingtime Blues;
Jingle Jinks; Nineties Swing.

Dances with a Scottish Flavour: Cameron Fling; Skirl of the Pipes;
Tartan Twinkle; Tartan Parade; Kiltie Sway; White Heather Parade;
Piper's Parade; Scottish Swing; Scotland the Brave.

(20) LET'S HAVE A CEILIDH – The Essential Guide to Scottish
Dancing by Robbie Shepherd. Music selected and arranged by Jim
Johnstone. Published by Canongate Press. Revised Edition 1996.
ISBN 0-86241-513-6. 118 pages. 196 x 126 mm. £5.99.
Steps for 25 popular Scottish dances are described in a simple,
easy-to-read form with suitable music.

Contents

Preface; Background to Dancing; A Life of Music and Dancing;
The Basic Steps; Grand March; Circassian Circle; Friendly Waltz;
Dashing White Sergeant; La-Va; Boston Two Step; Virginia Reel;
Highland Schottische; Four-Hand Star; Strip the Willow; Pride of
Erin Waltz; Eightsome Reel; Call of The Pipes; Mississippi Dip;
Scottish Reform; Eva Three Step; Lomond Waltz; Lancers; St.
Bernard's Waltz; Scottish Reform; The Canadian Barn Dance;
Britannia Two Step; Swedish Masquerade; Gay Gordons; Broun's
Reel.

(21) PARTY DANCES AND GAMES (ISTD).

Revised 1986. Reprinted 1998. 34 pages, 208 x 148 mm. Available from ISTD (See page 21) at £6.50 inclusive. Scripts of 34 dances with ideas for games for adults and children.

Contents

The Beeje	The Mod Barn Dance	The Birdie Dance
Bus Stop and 'Baby' Bus Stop	The Palais Glide Rowing	Party Boston Two Step Come to the Ceilidh
The Charleston Rag	Running on the Spot Dance	Disco Mixer Dance
The Cokey Cokey		The Farmer's Wife
The Conga	The Slosh	The Disco Hitch Hike
The Elephant Walk	Snoopy	Simple Simon Says
The Family Waltz	Soul Cha Cha Cha	Pit Pat (or Quack
The Gay Gordons	The Spanish Swing	Quack) Polka
Hand Jive and 'Sitting' Hand Jive	St. Bernard's Waltz Suzy	Skipping Disco Teddy Bears' Picnic
The Lambeth Walk	The Swinging Blues	"Baby" Veleta
March of the Mods	Zorbas Dance	

Team games, dancing competitions, The Charleston.

(22) PARTY DANCES AND GAMES (IDTA).

By Nancy Clarke. New edition 1994. 64 pages, 184 x 125 mm. £3.00 inclusive. Available from IDTA (see page 21 for address).

Contents

Ballin' the Jack	Conga	March of the Mods
Barn Dance – progressive	Dashing White Sergeant	Palais Glide Pattacake Polka
The Beejee	Didi Town Parade	Samba Miranda
Boomps a Daisy	Elephant Walk	Saturday Swing
Bossa Nova 66	Farmer's Wife Dance	St. Bernard's Waltz
Butlin's Ballet	Gay Gordons	Strut
Charleston Rag	Hip Over	Veleta – party version
Chestnut Tree	Hoppel Poppel	Virginia reel
Circle Waltz	Jackbot Jinx	Yearning Saunter –
1 2 3 Clap Clap	Knees Up Mother Brown	party version
Cokey Cokey or Hokey Cokey	Lambeth Walk	

DANCING FIGURES

So far the emphasis has been on dance scripts and material of direct relevance to sequence dancers. Nearly all books on social and ballroom dancing, however, deal with dancing figures rather than scripts. Since scripts consist of dancing figures joined together these books will obviously contain much information of value to the sequence dancer. When the instructor calls out 'open telemark' what steps are involved? What is the difference between a 'feather finish' and a 'feather ending'? A reliable source which gives details of steps and technique of figures will obviously have its uses especially for dancers hoping to gain awards and become professionals.

STANDARD DANCING FIGURES

Dancing figures are groups of steps ranging in size from the 1 step of the Reverse Pivot in the quickstep to the 30 steps of the Turkish Towel in the cha cha cha. Standard figures for a particular dance have been selected by ballroom dancing experts as being the best for general usefulness, style of performance and teaching purposes. They are the basis for the system of ballroom dancing awards for both modern and Latin-American dances. Unfortunately there are no standard figures for dances such as saunters, blues and swings and many figures commonly found in scripts do not appear in the teaching manuals.

LEARNING SEQUENCE DANCING FROM DANCING FIGURES

The books of instruction described so far have started with the performance and study of a particular sequence and worked back to an understanding of the dancing figures. An alternative approach used by teachers of ballroom dancing is to concentrate on each dancing figure in turn paying great attention to style and technique. Having mastered the figures it is not difficult to put them together to perform the various sequences. Two books which use this approach are described on the following pages.

15

(23) MODERN SEQUENCE DANCING FOR ALL.

Written and published by Thomas Alan Whitworth, Jan. 1994. Illustrated by Wilfrid Eaton. ISBN 0-9501927-3-2. 168 pages, 194 x 128 mm, b&w illustrations, index, table of abbreviations. Price £7.50 post free. Available from the author and many other suppliers.

As a guide to the theory and practice of modern and old-time sequence dancing, this book aims to answer some of the questions asked by both newcomers and more experienced dancers. The aim is not so much to teach dancing but rather to aid the instructor by providing material that can be studied away from the dance floor.

For the beginner the book provides a series of graded exercises that lead to the performance of a simple sequence dance. The author develops strategies for learning and remembering sequences with the help of appropriate examples. To aid the process of understanding and memorising, the text is illustrated with dancing figures which are classified by foot movements rather than by individual dances.

Throughout the text reference is made to Latin-American and old-time styles since under the present system, two thirds of new award-winning dances originate from these forms of dance.

The book also includes a chapter by Ken Fuller that sets out in some detail the development of the modern sequence style in the Manchester area from 1950 to 1965.

Contents

Introduction to modern sequence dancing; learning modern sequence dancing; abbreviations and technical matters; remembering sequence dances; standard dancing figures; walks and change figures; checks, rocks and hovers; whisks, wings and zig-zags; chassés, quarter turns and lock steps; dancing turns; the rumba and the cha cha cha; the various dances; the traditional old-time dances; finer points of technique; the growth of modern sequence dancing in the Manchester area (K. Fuller).

(24) AN INTRODUCTION TO SEQUENCE DANCING.

By Harry Horne. 1998. 68 pages, 208 x 148 mm. Obtainable from North Star Publishers, P.O. Box 20, Otley, Yorks., LS21 2SA, Tel: 01943 462269, at £7.95 inclusive.

The first half of this useful book deals with basic theory and technique and the fundamentals of old-time dancing. The remaining sections contain dancing figures for the modern waltz, foxtrot, quickstep, rumba, cha cha cha and jive; both man's and lady's steps are given. The book ends with a list of abbreviations and a short glossary.

Contents

Introduction
A brief history of dancing
Sequence dancing
New sequence dances
Learning to dance
Line of dance and alignments
The language of dancing
Style and technique
Balance, poise and body
   position
Leading
The Waltzes
Holds
Music, times and tempos
Descriptions of sequence
   dances
Positions of the feet

Footwork
The amount of turn
Rise and fall and body sway
Common heel movements
Steps of the old-time waltz
The bow and curtsy
Figures used in modern
   sequence waltzes
Modern sequence waltz
Modern sequence foxtrot
The quickstep
The tango
The rumba
The cha cha cha
The jive
List of abbreviations
Glossary

HISTORY OF SEQUENCE DANCING

Some sequence dancers are interested in the history of sequence dancing — they have often been dancing for many years and like to delve into the past. The history of sequence dancing has been largely neglected by writers on the history of social dance. (See pages 30–32 for books on the history of social and ballroom dancing.)

A recent work by T. A. Whitworth attempts to fill this gap by tracing the development of sequence dancing from Victorian times to the present day. It lists names and arrangers of sequence dances year by year up to and including 1994. Section II of this source book brings the list up-to-date to the year 2000. These books have indices including the names of nearly all the dances that can be allocated dates. Lists of this kind are very useful for competitors in inventive sequence dance competitions — they can ensure that the name of their new dance has not already been used for an earlier dance.

(25) A HISTORY OF SEQUENCE DANCING AND SCRIPT LIST.

Written and published by T. A. Whitworth, Oct. 1995, 224 pp, 210 x 148 mm. ISBN 0-9501927-4-0. £8.50 inclusive. Available from the author and other suppliers.

A history of sequence dancing from the Victorian era to the present day. More than 3000 dances are woven into a historical narrative. The three main sections cover dances up to 1945, from 1946 to 1974 and from 1975 to 1994. There are comments on many of the dances and minibiographies of important people in the sequence dancing world.

Contents

An overview of sequence dancing; the early years (period up to 1945); years of transition (1946–1974); the modern era (1975—1994); sequence dancing in perspective. Each of the three sections has a separate index of dances.

MISCELLANEOUS BOOKS.

(26) DANCE IN SEQUENCE – SMILE IN HARMONY.

Written and illustrated by Pat Price. Published by T. A. Whitworth (1997). 80pp, 210 x 148 mm, ISBN 0-9501927-6-7. £6.00 inclusive from T. A. Whitworth and other suppliers.

A volume of quirky verse that observes the foibles of the modern sequence dancer. This text is aimed at sequence dancers everywhere — it draws from the author's personal experience and is enlivened with original cartoons.

Contents

Retiring Gracefully; The Swinging Sixties; Weston-Super-Mare; Tea Dancing; The Newcomer; The Taxi Quickstep; Saturday Night; The Raffle; Crêpe Calypso; Ralph's Roving Eye; The Dancing Years; Last Waltz; New Fangled Tango; Overture; Pas de Deux; Postman's Knock; The Survivors; Songs of the Dancing Birds; Tea Dansant; Dance! And Grow Young!; Basil; Don't You Believe It!; Has Anyone Seen Grandma?; Edna; Stay as Sweet as you Are; The Thingamajig; It Does Seem Such A Pity; Bally Dancing!; Two Left Feet; The Blackpool Belle; Going Solo; Ronde de Jambe; The Beginners' Quadrille; Play it Again Sam!; Rock Around The Clock; For The Record; Housewife's Choice; Finale.

(27) THE WANDERING MINSTREL – BRYAN SMITH.

Written by June Smith (1996). 54 pages, 208 x 148 mm. ISBN 0-9527925-0-8. Obtainable fron June Smith, 27 Chapel Avenue, Addlestone, Surrey, KT15 1UH. £6.00

The musical life of Bryan Smith from the Village Hall to the Royal Albert Hall and Beyond.

Contents

The early days; Bryan the pianist; Bryan the soldier; Bryan the family man; Bryan the composer; Bryan the broadcaster; Bryan the sailor.

BOOKS FOR KEEN SEQUENCE DANCERS

Many sequence dancers see their dancing as no more than a pleasant social activity – scripts, books and videos are not for them. Others, however, feel an urge to extend their knowledge of sequence dancing and improve their performance. Some may aspire to gain dancing qualifications and possibly become teachers of sequence dancing or competitors in inventive dance competitions. Various technical manuals are available written by experts and recommended by dancing associations for those studying for awards. These set out both theory and recommended technique. They contain charts of the standard dancing figures which give not only steps and orientations but also footwork, sway and rise and fall. Although written mainly for aspiring professionals they form a useful source of reference for the ordinary sequence dancer.

(28) BALLROOM DANCING.

By Alex Moore. Published by A. and C. Black. 9th edition. Reprinted 1992. 336 pages, 190 x 125 mm. Hardback. ISBN 0-7136-2794-8.

Available from Ballroom Dancing Times Book Service (see page 21) at £13.04 inclusive.

This book has undergone several revisions since it was first published in 1936. It is notable for its accuracy, clarity of style and excellent foot diagrams of dancing figures. Alex Moore was a most successful dancer and writer who played a great part in the development of modern ballroom techniques. In 1933 he started a Letter Service which provided a complete service for dance teachers — now provided by DanceSport International.

Contents

Foreword; Preface; Introductory Section; The Quickstep; The Waltz; The Foxtrot; The Tango; For the Keen Dancer; Popular Dances; Ballroom Novelty Dances and Games.

TECHNICAL MANUALS FOR DANCING AWARDS

The general standard of ballroom dancing has improved tremendously since the introduction of Amateur Medal Tests. Any qualified teacher can enter a student for a medal test or a dancer may enter directly through one of the ballroom associations.

Most of the manuals have been produced by two societies:–

(a)   ISTD Sales Office, Imperial House, 22/26 Paul Street, London, EC2A 4QE. Tel: 020 7377 1577. Fax: 020 7247 6728.

(b)   International Sales (IDTA), 76 Bennett Road, Brighton, BN2 5JL. Tel: 01273 608583. Fax: 01273 674388.

Other sources of these books are:—

(c)   Dance Books, 15 Cecil Court, London, WC2N 4EZ. Tel: 020 7836 2314. Fax: 020 7497 0473.

(d)   Ballroom Dancing Times Book Service, Clerkenwell House, 45-47 Clerkenwell Green, London, EC1R 0EB. Tel: 020 7250 3006. Fax: 020 7253 6679.

(e)   Dance Sport International Ltd., The Courtyard, Aurelia Road, Croydon, Surrey, CR0 3BF. Tel: 020 8664 8188. Fax: 020 8664 8288. (Sometimes known as Hearn and Spencer.)

(f)   Worldwide Record Distributors Ltd., 282 Camden Road, London, NW1 9AB. Tel: 020 7267 6762. Fax: 020 7482 4029.

In the 1980's it was hoped that all the teachers' organisations would adopt the same syllabus for their tests — unfortunately this has not materialised although the differences are comparatively minor. There are separate groups of manuals for the ballroom dances (Quickstep, Waltz, Foxtrot and Tango) and the Latin-American dances.

Prices tend to increase over the years and it is wise to check the cost and availability of items. (Some guidance on ordering materials by post and from booksellers is given later in the book.)

21

ISTD PUBLICATIONS

(29) THE REVISED TECHNIQUE OF BALLROOM DANCING.

By Alex Moore. Published by ISTD. 10th Edition. 1995.
108 pages, 214 x 138 mm.

First published by ISTD in October 1948, this book adapts some of
the material in Alex Moore's 'Ballroom Dancing' (28) to suit the
syllabus requirements of the ISTD. Although now out of print many
copies are to be found in second-hand bookshops.

Contents

Preface; How to Study the Charts; Associate Syllabus and Standard
Variations for the Quickstep, Waltz, Foxtrot and Tango; the Named
Variations for the Fellowship Syllabus; Appendix; TheWalks;
Approved Endings to the Named Variations.

(30) THE BALLROOM TECHNIQUE. Published by ISTD. 1994.
134 pages, 210 x 148 mm. £11.50 inclusive.

This volume is essentially a revised and extended version of (29)
produced by a committee of the Ballroom Faculty of the ISTD
following the death of Alex Moore.

Contents

Preface; Training for Professional Examinations; How to Study the
Charts; Waltz; Foxtrot; Quickstep; Tango; Additional Figures.

(31) POPULAR VARIATIONS.

Written and published by Alex Moore. November 1989. 124 pages,
215 x 137 mm. £6.50 inclusive.

A book for the expert ballroom dancer. Single dancing figures and
suggested amalgamations are set out for the Waltz (57), Foxtrot (64),
Tango (52) and Quickstep (57). Some examples for the waltz are
'Promenade Ronde, R. Lunge Point to Whisk'; 'The Double
Whisk';'The Telespin'; 'Syncopated Spins and Twist'.

(32) QUESTIONS AND ANSWERS FOR THE ISTD ASSOCIATE EXAMINATION. Devised by Elizabeth Romain. Published by Hearn and Spencer Ltd. 1991. 32 pages, 208 x 148 mm. See (33).

Includes Waltz, Quickstep, Tango and Slow Foxtrot.

(33) QUESTIONS AND ANSWERS.

Devised by Elizabeth Romain. (1997). 4 books for Waltz, Quickstep, Tango and Foxtrot written to replace (32). Published by DanceSport International Ltd. Each 208 x 148 mm. 24 pages. £7.95 inclusive.

Written for ISTD Ballroom Students at all three grades.

(34) THE REVISED TECHNIQUE OF LATIN AMERICAN DANCING. Published by ISTD. 5th Edition enlarged 1983. 192 pages, 248 x 154 mm. £10.00 inclusive. Now replaced by (35).

(35) LATIN AMERICAN TECHNIQUE (ISTD).

4 books for Rumba, Cha Cha Cha, Paso Doble, Samba (Jive may follow). Published by ISTD to replace (34). Each 248 x 153 mm. About 128 pages. £7.00 inclusive.

The official books for the ISTD examinations.

(36) POPULAR VARIATIONS IN LATIN-AMERICAN DANCING. Published by ISTD. Edited by Elizabeth Romain. 1982. 68 pages, 208 x 145 mm. £5.50 inclusive. (Based on 'Latin Variations' by Elizabeth Romain, 1972).

Single dancing figures and some amalgamations are set out for the Rumba (14), Samba (16), Paso Doble (8), Jive (15) and Cha Cha (13).

Examples from the Rumba are 'Advanced Leg Turns'; 'Continuous Hip Twists'; 'Horse and Cart'.

(37) QUESTIONS AND ANSWERS FOR THE ISTD LATIN ASSOCIATE EXAMINATION. Devised by Elizabeth Romain. Published by DanceSport International Ltd. 1989. 42 pages. 208 x 145 mm. £7.95 inclusive.

Questions and answers for the Associate Examinations in the Rumba, Samba, Paso Doble, Jive and Cha Cha Cha.

I.D.T.A. PUBLICATIONS

(38) (a) **TECHNIQUE OF BALLROOM DANCING** by Guy Howard. Published by IDTA. New Edition 1986. Reprinted 1987. 86 pages, 240 x 180 mm. ISBN 0-900326-19-0.

(b) **TECHNIQUE OF BALLROOM DANCING** by Guy Howard. Published by IDTA. New Edition 1992. 248 x 182 mm. Hardback. ISBN 0-900326-19-0. £16.00 inclusive.

This is a revised and extended version of book (a) in hardback.

See page 21 for the address of International Sales (IDTA).

Contents

Foreword; Introduction; General Notes and Descriptions of Headings; Dancing figures for Associate, Member and Fellowship Grades for Waltz, Quickstep, Foxtrot and Tango; Social Rhythm Foxtrot; Index.

(39) **QUESTIONS AND ANSWERS ON THE TECHNIQUE OF BALLROOM DANCING** by Guy Howard. Published by Christine Howard, 1995. 48 pages, 210 x 148 mm. ISBN 0-9526237-0-6. £7.25 inclusive.

Obtainable from IDTA or from Christine Howard, Mena Farm, Lanivet, Cornwall, PL30 5HW. Tel/Fax: 01208 831845.

Contents

Foreword; Introduction; Preface; Hints for Candidates; Questions and Answers for the Waltz, Quickstep, Foxtrot, Tango; Associateship, Membership and Fellowship; List of Abbreviations.

(40) **TECHNIQUE OF LATIN DANCING.**

By Walter Laird. New Edition 1988. Reprinted 1990. 186 pages, 248 x 184 mm. Hardback. ISBN 0 900 326 21 2. £17.00 inclusive.

Essential reading for teachers, coaches and dancers of all grades.

Contents

Foreword; Preface; Chronicle; General; First Principles; Basic Positions; Rumba; Samba; Paso Doble; Cha Cha Cha; Jive; Suggested Amalgamations; Index.

24

(41) I.D.T.A. SUPPLEMENT TO THE TECHNIQUE OF LATIN DANCING.

By Walter Laird. Published by IDTA. 1st edition 1997. Reprinted 1998. 64 pages. 240 x 178 mm. £9.95 inclusive.

This volume includes those figures listed in Appendix I of the BDC Rule Book which do not form part of the IDTA Latin Syllabus.

Contents

Preface; Abbreviations; Charts of Dancing Figures for the Rumba, Samba, Paso Doble Cha Cha Cha and Jive.

British Dance Council; Appendix I (Latin); I.D.T.A. Latin Syllabus.

(42) THE ROAD TO SUCCESS IN MODERN BALLROOM PROFESSIONAL EXAMINATIONS.

Written and published by Alex Brown, 1999. 120 pages, 210 x 150 mm. £12.00 inclusive.

Order from the author, Alex Brown at 6 Guildford Avenue, Walton, Chesterfield, S40 3NB. Also available from Dancesport International or from Ballroom Dancing Times Book Service (see page 18).

A handbook on the technique of ballroom dancing for the use of candidates for both the IDTA and ISTD examinations.

Contents

Introduction; A condensed history of modern ballroom technique; Explanations of foot positions, alignment, amount of turn, direction, rise and fall, footwork, sway and technical terms; Questions and answers for the examinations for the student, associate, membership/ licentiateship and fellowship examinations; Teaching ability; The ISTD examination technique; The future development of technique.

BALLROOM AND SOCIAL DANCING BOOKS

These differ from the technical manuals so far described in providing more explanation of the dancing figures involved by way of foot diagrams, illustrations and photographs — they are not constrained by the need to follow an examination syllabus.

The following books may be purchased from Dance Books or the Ballroom Dancing Times Book Service. Addresses on page 21.

(43) MODERN BALLROOM DANCING.

By Victor Silvester. New edition 1993. Revised and updated by Bryan Allen. Published by Stanley Paul, London. 234 pages, 253 x 195 mm. Hardback. ISBN 0-09-178193-0. £19.99 inclusive.

The original book written in 1927 was reprinted 25 times by 1941 — it became the standard manual for young adults in 1940's when ballroom dancing was a popular diversion. It has undergone many revisions although it retains much of the original material. Later versions include a history section based on 'The Art of Ballroom Dancing' by Victor Silvester and Philip J. S. Richardson (1936). The latest edition revised by Bryan Allen gives detailed instructions for performing the dancing figures, some being illustrated by foot diagrams. There are more than 30 full-page colour pictures of professional dancers. (Victor Silvester died in 1978.)

Contents

I   History: The development of the two techniques; How dances begin; Just before the 1914 war; Jazz; 1914 – 1918; 1918 to the first 'worlds'; The coming of technique; The 1930's to the present.

II Practice: On dancing; Social dancing; Slow and quick rhythms; Easy waltz; More advanced technique; Waltz; Foxtrot; Quickstep; Tango; Viennese Waltz; Rumba; Samba; Cha Cha Cha; Paso Doble; Rock 'n' Roll; Jive or American Swing; Disco dancing.

(44) THE JOY OF DANCING — BALLROOM, LATIN
AND ROCK/JIVE FOR ABSOLUTE BEGINNERS.

By Peggy Spencer. Published by Chameleon Books. (1997).
128 pages, 260 x 218 mm. Hardback. Ring Binding.
ISBN 233-98173-5. £14.99 inclusive.
A workbook for social dancers. Many colour photographs and useful
hints. Video called 'Absolute Beginners' available. See (72)c on
page 40.
Contents
Introduction; General advice; Waltz; Mamba; Foxtrot; Samba; Tango;
Cha Cha Cha; Quickstep; Merengue; Rock/Jive; Rumba; Wedding
Waltz; Glossary.

(45) THE JOY OF DANCING — THE NEXT STEPS.
Ballroom, Latin and Jive for Social Dancers of all ages.
By Peggy Spencer. Published by Chameleon Books, 1999.
128 pages, 260 x 218 mm. Hardback. Ring Binding.
ISBN 0-233-99488-2. £16.99 inclusive.
Ballroom, Latin and Jive for Social Dancers of all ages. Illustrated
with colour photographs. A continuation volume to (44) above in
the same format. Video 'The Next Steps' available. See (72)c on
page 40.
Contents
Introduction; Waltz; Mambo; Foxtrot; Samba; Tango; Cha Cha Cha;
Quickstep; Merengue; Jive; Rumba; Glossary of Terms; Why Join a
Dancing School; Useful Contacts and Information.

(46) THE BALLROOM DANCE PACK.
By Walter Laird. Published by Dorling Kindersley (1994). 80 pages,
280 x 235 mm. Hardback. ISBN 0-7513-0079-9. £19.99 inclusive.
Includes CD, Step-cards and Feet templates.
Contents
How to use the pack; Waltz; Quickstep; Tango; Cha Cha Cha; Samba;
Rumba; Glossary; Figures; Amalgamations and routines; Leading
and following; What shall I wear?; Acknowledgements.

27

(47) FIRST STEPS TO BALLROOM DANCING.

By Lyndon Wainwright. Published by Lyric Books (1993). 80 pages, 296 x 210 mm. ISBN 0-7-111-0089-6. £8.99 imclusive.

Contents

How to learn; First steps – Social Foxtrot and Cha Cha Cha; Definitions; Waltz; Samba; Quickstep; Jive; More Cha Cha Cha; Rumba; More Social Foxtrot.

(48) START BALLROOM AND LATIN DANCING FOR ADULTS.
Written and drawn by Jed Malins. Published by Dance Books Ltd., London (1991). 56 pages, 210 x 297 mm. ISBN 1-85273-029-3. £7.00 inclusive.

A highly original book printed and illustrated with cartoons by the author; gives many useful tips for beginners.

Contents

Waltz; Quickstep; Cha Cha Cha; Jive; Rock 'n' Roll; Slow Rhythm.

(49) TEACH YOURSELF BALLROOM DANCING.

I.S.T.D. Published by Hodder and Stoughton (1992). 182 pages, 196 x 128 mm. ISBN 0-340-5-162-4. £7.99 inclusive.

A handy-size book first published in 1977 – the work of Peggy Spencer and others. It has some diagrams of holds but consists mainly of charts of dancing with explanatory notes — it does not waste space on coloured photographs.

There is a good historical introduction to each dance.

Contents
Foreword; Introduction; How to study dances and individual figures.
Ballroom Dances: Waltz, Social Foxtrot, Tango, Social Quickstep, Quickstep, Quick Waltz.
Latin-American Dances: Rumba, Samba, Paso Doble, Jive, Rock 'n' Roll, Cha Cha Cha.
Pop and Social Dances: Solo Dancing – Disco Style, Bossa Nova, Merengue, Mambo.
Organisations worldwide.

(50) THE SOCIAL DANCE SURVIVAL GUIDE.

By Ken Akrill. Published by Sigma Press (1988). 146 pages, 210 x 148 mm. ISBN 1-85058-611-X. £8.40. inclusive.

Contents

What is Social Dancing? The Ballroom Dances: Waltz; Viennese Waltz; Social Foxtrot; Tango. The Latin Dances: Merengue; Cha Cha Cha; Salsa; Mambo; Rumba; Samba. Dances for Discos: Night Club Swing; Slosh; Macarena. Music for Dancing.

(51) DANCE CRAZY SERIES OF BOOKS. All written by Paul Bottomer and published by Lorenz Books (1996 onwards). 64 pages, 207 x 207 mm. Hardback. Each volume £4.95 inclusive.

Quickstep	ISBN 1-85967-3937
Waltz	ISBN 1-85967-3961
Rock 'n' Roll	ISBN 1-85967-2264
Line Dancing	ISBN 1-85967-2310
Mambo and Merengue	ISBN 1-85967-3945
Samba and Lambada	ISBN 1-85967-3953
Salsa	ISBN 1-85967-2213
Tango Argentino	ISBN 1-85967-2167

(52) HOW TO DANCE

By Paul Bottomer, Lorenz Books (1998). Hardback. 256 pages, 304 x 238 mm. ISBN 1-85967-8319. £17.95 inclusive.

This large heavy volume uses material from the 'Dance Crazy' series above. Each dance has a good historical introduction.

Contents

Introduction; Tango; Merengue; Salsa; Lambada; Samba; Reggae; Mambo; Cha Cha Cha; Paso Doble; Samba; Jive; Waltz; Quickstep; Modern Tango; Slow Foxtrot; Viennese Waltz; Further information; Index.

These books are available from Worldwide Record Distributors Ltd., 282 Camden Road, London, NW1 9AB. Tel: 020 7267 6762. Fax: 020 7482 4029 and other booksellers.

THE HISTORY OF POPULAR DANCING

Some of the books described earlier include accounts of the history of popular dancing.

(43) *'Modern Ballroom Dancing'* by Victor Silvester (p. 26) has a 30-page introductory chapter on the development of social dance.

(49) *'Teach Yourself Ballroom Dancing'*, I.S.T.D., (p. 28).

(52) *'Dance Crazy – How to Dance'* by Paul Bottomer (p. 29).

The three books above have historical notes on the dances they describe. Paul Bottomley's book includes some of the more recent social dances such as the salsa, mambo, merengue and lambada.

The following texts give more detailed accounts of the development and origins of the social and ballroom dancing. They may be obtained from booksellers such as The Ballroom Dancing Times Book Service.

(53) MAY I HAVE THE PLEASURE – THE STORY OF POPULAR DANCING.

Written by Belinda Quirey with Steve Bradshaw and Ronald Smedley. Published by Dance Books, 15 Cecil Court, London, WC2N 4EZ. Tel: 020 7836 2314. Fax: 020 7497 0473. (1987. Reprinted 1993). 124 pages, 233 x 177 mm. ISBN 1-85273-000-5.

Contents

Introduction. From our roots to the Renaissance. The French connection. The century of waltz. Cheek to cheek. Let's twist again. The people's dances. Glossary. Booklist.

(54) A BRIEF REVIEW OF ONE HUNDRED YEARS.

By Bryan Issac. Published by BATD (1992). 218 pages, 215 x 150 mm. Hardback. (Limited edition of 2000 copies.) £14.50 inclusive.

Contents

Foreword. Acknowledgments. The founders, presidents and officers of the British Association of Teachers of Dancing. A short history of dance. 1892–1916. 1917–1941. 1942–1967. 1968–1992. Obituary.

(55) THE STORY OF BRITISH POPULAR DANCE.

By Lyndon Wainwright. Published by IDTA (circa 1997). 66 pages, 296 x 210 mm. ISBN 0-900326-35-2. £11.00 inclusive.

Contents

Foreword; Preface; The author.

I   Earliest days. George I – Victoria. Early years of the 20th century. Early championships.

II   The dance develops. A time of changes. Technique and authority. Consolidation.

III Popular dancing. Latin Dance. Music, teaching and novelty dances.

IV World War II, Dance in print. Television.

V   The post-war revolution. Dance teaching. Mutations. Non-syllabus dances. Technique again.

VI Politics. Competitions and competitors. Personal observations.

Appendices. Index of dances. Index of names.

(56) OH, HOW WE DANCED: THE HISTORY OF BALLROOM DANCING IN SCOTLAND.

By Elizabeth Casciani. Published by the Mercat Press, Edinburgh (1994). 150 pages, 235 x 155 mm. ISBN 1-873644-29-9.

A well-presented account of the history of ballroom dancing in Scotland illustrated with photographs. It contains many references, a list of ballrooms and an index.

Contents

List of illustrations; Preface; Aristocratic assemblies in the 18th century; Popular assemblies in the 19th century; Growth of dancing schools (1900–1910); Flappers and foxtrots (1910–1920); Rise of the big palais ballrooms (1920-1930); Big bands and scandals (1930–1940); Crooners and championships (1940–1950); From couples to individuals (1950 to the present); Epilogue – the end of an era?; Notes to the text; Appendices; Index.

31

(57) THE WORLD OF PHYLLIS HAYLOR AND BALLROOM DANCING. Edited by Bryan Allen. Published by ISTD (1984). 248 pages, 250 x 174 mm. paperback, £6.30 inclusive. Hardback, £7.40 inclusive. Obtainable from ISTD Sales. (See page 21.)

Contents

Articles on the history and development of the English style of ballroom dancing. These include 'The Ballroom Scene — 1945', 'Past Versus Present 1956', 'Development of the Left Whisk 1960', 'Nomenclature — 1973', 'The Cluster Series — 1980'.

Other useful books on the development of ballroom and sequence dancing unfortunately now out of print are:—

(58) SOCIAL DANCE — A SHORT HISTORY by A. H. Franks. Published by Routledge Kegan Paul (1963). 236 pages, 250 x 160 mm. Hardback.

Contents

Acknowledgements. Introduction. The 15th, 16th, 17th, 18th, 19th, and 20th centuries. Appendices. Index.

(59) THE SOCIAL DANCES OF THE NINETEENTH CENTURY IN ENGLAND by Philip J. S. Richardson. Published by Herbert Jenkins (1960). 152 pages, 220 x 145 mm. Hardback.

Contents

Introduction. Assembly rooms. Some dances prior to the 19th century. The early years (1801–1815). After Waterloo (1815–1860). The second quarter (1825–1850). The polka craze (1843). Some mid-century dances (1843–1865). Some mid-century programmes. The second half (1865–1900). The original steps as danced.

(60) THE HISTORY OF ENGLISH BALLROOM DANCING (1910–1945) by Philip J. S. Richardson. Published by Herbert Jenkins (circa 1946). 168 pages, 220 x 145 mm. Hardback.

Contents

Preface. From 1910 to 1918. From armistice to Charleston (1918–1927). The basic technique is formed (1927–1934). The final phase (1934–1945). Dancing politics. Addenda. Index.

DANCING PERIODICALS

(61) SEQUENCE DANCING WORLD. Published by North Star Publishers. Editor Derek Arnold. P.O. Box 20, Otley, West Yorks., LS21 2SA. Tel: 01943 462269.

A forum of discussion of matters relating to old-time and modern sequence dancing — articles, letters, details of CD and video releases etc. — usually 10 issues per year. Free to subscribers to the script service but can be bought separately. Annual subscription £28.00.

(62) BALLROOM DANCING TIMES. Published by Dancing Times Ltd., Clerkenwell House, 45-47 Clerkenwell Green, London, EC1R 0EB. Tel. 020 7250 3006. Fax 020 7253 6679. Editor Mary Clarke.

Mainly for ballroom dancers but includes scripts of new winning sequence dances with comments and a regular feature on sequence dancing. Includes items from the Book Service Section (see page 21).

Published monthly. Price £1.10. Annual subscription £17.00.

(63) DANCE DIARY (see page 1).

Eddie Foulds and Olive Elderton, 30 The Crescent, Welwyn, Herts., AL6 9JQ. Tel/Fax: 01438 840066. Mobile: 07974 258217. A magazine for ballroom, tea and sequence dancers in London and South East England. 4 issues per year. Annual subscription £7.00.

(64) DANCE NEWS. (John and Arlene Leach).

Hamble House, Meadrow, Godalming, Surrey, GU7 3HJ.

Tel. 01483 428679. Fax 01483 417650.

A weekly newspaper for dancers — competitions, ballroom dancing news. Every Thursday, price £1.00. Annual subscription £59.00.

(65) DANCE TEACHER (IDTA).

International Sales Ltd., International House, 76 Bennet Road, Brighton, BN5 5JL. Edited by Jay Dearling. Tel. 01273 685652. Fax 01273 674388.

The only monthly magazine for qualified professional teachers of dancing. Free to members of IDTA; £48 per annum for others.

YEAR BOOKS

(66) DANCING YEAR BOOK 2000. Published annually by IDTA since 1947. 164 pages. 210 x 148 mm. £15.00. (IDTA address on page 21).

(67) DANCE WORLD DIRECTORY, Vol. II. 326 pages, 210 x 148 mm. £9.99 plus postage. An international handbook. Available from Dance World Directory, P.O. Box 366, Croydon, Surrey, CRO 2SF. Tel/Fax: 020 8239 7180.

MUSIC FOR SEQUENCE DANCING SESSIONS

A list of musicians specialising in sequence appears in each issue of the North Star magazine 'Sequence Dancing World'. (See pages 3 and 33). Most sequence dance leaders however prefer to use recorded music since this is cheaper and gives more control and flexibility. Most leaders have changed to CD's which have numerous advantages although some still use their stocks of records and tapes. A recent development is the mini-disc which is about half the size of a CD but stores up to $2^1/_2$ hours of music. Not much pre-recorded music is available in this format but leaders can record their own! Many of the major suppliers also sell videos, books and related materials.

(a)   Suppliers already mentioned are ISTD, IDTA, DanceSport International, Worldwide Record Distributors Ltd., Ballroom Dancing Times Book Service (addresses on p.21), Brockbank Lane (p. 1), Northern Dance Services (page 2).

(b)   Maestro Direct, P.O. Box 2255, Mitcham, Surrey, CR4 3BG. Tel: 020 8687 2008. Fax: 020 8687 1998.

(c)   Savoy Music, P.O. Box 271, Purley, Surrey, CR8 4YL. Tel: 01737 554739. Fax: 01737 556737.

(d)   Tema International, Music and Dance, 151 Nork Way, Banstead, Surrey, SM7 1HR. Tel: 01737 219607. Fax: 01737 219609.

(e)   C and D Dance Records, 145 Chestnut Avenue, Eastleigh, SO50 5BB. Tel: 023 8061 4476. Fax: 023 8034 2328.

(f)   Dance and Listen Ltd., 1 Queen's Road, Fleet, Hampshire, GU13 9LA. Tel: 01252 629740. Fax: 01252 811788.

SUPPLIERS OF VARIABLE SPEED AUDIO EQUIPMENT

Although devices for playing recorded music are available from many sources there are some advantages in dealing with a specialist supplier.

(a)   Keytronics Professional Limited, 87 Station Road, Alsager, Stoke-on-Trent, ST7 2PF.   Tel: 07000 823594. Fax: 0870 706 4416.

Keytronics is a small family business engaged in manufacturing, selling and maintaining equipment designed especially for dance leaders. They supply computers and are developing internet services for dancers. A free booklet 'Computers — How They Work' is available on request.

(b)   Portogram Ltd., 212 High Street, Barnet, Herts., EN5 5SZ. Tel: 020 8449 4183. Fax: 020 8440 1029.

Portogram have been manufacturing variable speed audio equipment since 1945. Their products are also available from International Sales. (Address on page 21.)

VIDEOS

The increased availability of video recording and playing devices has been a great boon to dancers. Being able to watch experts performing the various sequences and dancing figures at leisure in one's home adds a great deal to the static representations of foot diagrams and still photographs.

The video catalogue of the Worldwide Record Distributors Ltd. (see page 21) has more than 200 entries covering elementary and advanced dancing, lectures, competitions, congress events, shows and choreography. The videos reviewed in the following pages deal mainly with sequence dancing although some recordings on social dancing and examination technique have been included.

Most videos sold in the UK use the PAL recording system; there is usually an extra charge for products designed for the NTSC system used in the USA and Japan. Some modern video players can be switched to either version. Video tapes may eventually be replaced by Digital Versatile Tapes (DVD's) which provide improved picture quality and sound and store more information.

SEQUENCE DANCING VIDEOS

(68) 'OBSERVE AND LEARN' SEQUENCE DANCING VIDEOS.
10 volumes of dances with 5 dances per video. £17.00 each inclusive.

Endorsed by the British Council of Dancing and the United Kingdom Alliance (UKA). Expert tuition and commentaries are by Glyn and Anne Watkins. Music by Bryan Smith and his Radio Orchestra and others.

Contents

Volume 1: The Veleta. Saunter Revé. Tango Serida. Wedgewood Blue Gavotte. Military Two Step.

Volume 2: Regis Waltz. Britannia Saunter. Tango Solair. La Mascotte. Rialto Two Step.

Volume 3: Engagement Waltz. Lancaster Tango. Glenroy Foxtrot. Quando Quickstep. Balmoral Blues.

Volume 4: Helenbrooke Waltz. Tango El Cid. Claringo Foxtrot. Universal Quickstep. Ragtime Swing.

Volume 5: Lilac Waltz. Square Tango. Saunter Together. Boston Two Step. Sindy Swing.

Volume 6: Woodside Waltz. Torque Tango. Karen Foxtrot. Mayfair Quickstep. Cheney Blues.

Volume 7: Rumba Dominique. Brazilian Samba. Paso Madrid. Sally Anne Cha Cha Cha. Let's Jive.

Volume 8: Blue Mosque Rumba. Social Samba. Paso Deena. Niki Cha Cha Cha. Coca Rola Jive.

Volume 9: Westmount Waltz. Tango Tarquilla. Jayde Foxtrot. Eivona Quickstep. Stephanne Blues.

Volume 10: Sovereign Waltz. Tango Las Vegas. Saunter Sonata. Society Two Step. Empress Mazurka.

Produced by Westport (UK) Limited, P.O. Box 15, Keynsham, Bristol, BS31 1XU. Tel: 0117 986 4097. Fax: 0117 986 4174. Website: http://www.westport.co.uk
Main Agent:
Tema International, Music and Dance, 151 Nork Way, Banstead, Surrey, SM7 1HR. Tel: 01737 219607. Fax: 01737 219609 (Suppliers of CD's, videos, dance shoes, etc.).
Available also from many other suppliers.

(69) A BEGINNER'S GUIDE TO SEQUENCE DANCING. 8 volumes. £17.00 each volume inclusive.
Demonstrated by Ted and Sue Burroughs. A CD with suitable music is available for each video. Miniscripts are also included.
Contents
Volume 1: SAV 101V.
Mayfair Quickstep. Balmoral Blues. Tango Serida. Catherine Waltz. Together Saunter. Sindy Swing. Sally Ann Cha Cha. Iris Foxtrot. Let's Jive. Rumba One. MUSIC SAV 262CD. 20 tracks. £13.00 inclusive.
Volume 2: SAV 102V (Old Time Dancing).
The Veleta. Lilac Waltz. Boston Two Step. Square Tango. Barn Dance. St. Bernard's Waltz. Yearning Saunter. Military Two Step. Pride of Erin Waltz. Gay Gordons. MUSIC SAV 263CD. 20 tracks. £13.00 inclusive.
Volume 3: SAV 103V.
Emmerdale Waltz. Blue Bayou Rumba. Red Rose Saunter. Sizzlers Samba. Ragtime Swing. Mambo Magic. Tango Solair.
MUSIC SAV 299CD. 21 tracks. £13.75 inclusive.
Volume 4: SAV 104V.
Woodside Waltz. Rumba Beguine. Saunter Revé. Melody Foxtrot. Georgella Blues. Jacqueline Cha Cha. Jetta Jive. MUSIC SAV 300CD. 21 tracks. £13.75 inclusive.

Volume 5: SAV 105V.
Bluebird Waltz. Miami Rumba. Bossa Nova Blues. Glenroy Foxtrot. Quality Quickstep. Niki Cha Cha. Bambi Blues.
MUSIC SAV 303CD. 21 tracks. £13.75 inclusive.

Volume 6: SAV 106V.
Engagement Waltz. Roundabout Rumba. Shelley Saunter. Hot Spot Jive. Quando Quickstep. Las Vegas Tango. Caribbean Foxtrot.

Volume 7: SAV 107V.
Elizabeth's Waltz. Queen of Hearts Rumba. Sovereign Saunter. Mardi Gras Cha Cha. Broadway Quickstep. Jasmine Foxtrot. Cheney Blues.

Volume 8: SAV 108V.
Willow Wood Waltz. Sea Breeze Foxtrot. Elderberry Quickstep. Tango 44. Gin Swing. Cocabola Cha Cha. Millennium Rumba.

Music for volumes 6, 7 and 8 on SAV 308 CD. Produced and distributed by Savoy Music, P.O. Box 271, Purley, Surrey, CR8 4YL. Tel: 01737 554739. Fax: 01737 556737. Available also from Maestro Direct and many other suppliers.

(70) INSTEP DANCE VIDEOS — MODERN SEQUENCE COLLECTION. 16 volumes. £16.50 each inclusive.
Complete 90 minute programmes of visual instruction with music, presented by former World Champions Ian and Ruth Walker.
Most volumes have three dances per video.

Contents
Volume 1: Square Tango. Rumba Royal. Saunter Together,
Volume 2: Mayfair Quickstep. Rumba One. Bambi Blues.
Volume 3: Sally Ann Cha Cha. Sindy Swing. Balmoral Blues.
Volume 4: Waltz Catherine. Woodside Waltz. Lilac Waltz.
Volume 5: Saunter Revé. Tango Serida. Ragtime Swing.
Volume 6: Emmerdale Waltz. Waltz Marie. Tango Solair.

Volume 7: Melody Foxtrot. Glenroy Foxtrot. Jacqueline Cha Cha.

Volume 8: Saga Waltz. Magenta Waltz. Engagement Waltz.

Volume 9: Broadway Quickstep. Quando Quickstep. Universal Quickstep.

Volume 10: Redrose Saunter. Iris Foxtrot. Sharon Swing.

Volume 11: Tina Tango. Lola Tango. Tango El Cid.

Volume 12: Sweetheart Waltz. Breakaway Blues. Britannia Saunter. Georgella Blues.

Volume 13: Bluebird Waltz. Oriana Waltz. Waltz Cerise.

Volume 14: Rumba Deargo. Miami Rumba. Rosewood Rumba.

Volume 15: Barbados Cha Cha. Niki Cha Cha. Mahogany Cha Cha.

Volume 16: Valentine Saunter. Safron Swing. Mambo Magic.

Available from Maestro Direct, P.O. Box 2255, Mitcham, Surrey, CR4 3BG. Tel: 020 8687 2008. Fax: 020 8687 1998. Also from Worldwide Record Distributors Ltd. and other suppliers.

(71) AN INTRODUCTION TO MODERN SEQUENCE DANCING by Derek Young.

2 Quasar Videos:— Old Time (Q26) and Modern (Q27). £39.95 each inclusive.

Suitable for both beginners and more advanced dancers.

Contents

Q26 (Old Time) 16 dances.

Technical Waltz. Veleta. Fylde Waltz. Regis Waltz. Britannia Saunter. Saunter Revé. La Mascotte. Latchford Schottische. Gainsborough Glide. Lola Tango. Tango Solair. Midnight Tango. Military Two Step. Boston Two Step. Premier Two Step. Rialto Two Step.

Q27 (Official Modern Sequence) 32 dances.

Blue Mosque Rumba. Caribbean Rumba. Rumba One. Rumba Bianco. Marquesa Rumba. Sapphire Samba. Shadow Samba. Samba Katrina. Rosita Cha Cha. Sally Ann Cha Cha. Y.C. Cha Cha. Tutti Frutti Cha Cha. Paso Madrid. Paso Deena. Jubilee Live. Jupiter Jive.

Justa Jive. Eivonna Quickstep. Quando Quickstep. Universal Quickstep. Rayen Waltz. Helen Brooke Waltz. Woodside Waltz. Waltz Caravelle. Engagement Waltz. Rosslyn Foxtrot. Glenroy Foxtrot. Benita Foxtrot. Claringo Foxtrot. Tango El Cid. Tango Tarquilla. Tango Victoria.

Available from Quasar Videos, 'One Eleven', Hoarwithy, Hereford, HR2 6QH. Tel: 01432 840254. Fax: 01432 840227.

VIDEOS FOR BALLROOM DANCERS.

(72) PEGGY SPENCER VIDEOS.

(a)   BALLROOM DANCING FOR BEGINNERS. VC 6169.

Two basic figures in the Waltz, Jive Rock, Rhythm Foxtrot, Quickstep and Tango. 60 mins. £16.50 inclusive.

(b)   LATIN-AMERICAN DANCING FOR BEGINNERS. VC 6170.

Two basic figures in the Cha Cha Cha, Mambo, Rumba, Samba and Merengue. 60 mins. £16.50 inclusive.

(c)   THE NEXT STEPS. (Face the Video and Dance.)

Volume 1. VC 6600. Waltz, Cha Cha Cha, Quickstep, Rock Jive.

Volume 2. VC 6601. Slow Foxtrot, Rumba, Tango, Salsa/Mambo/ Samba.

Each volume £16.50 inclusive.

These videos are associated with Peggy Spencer's Joy of Dancing Books 'Ballroom, Latin and Rock/Jive for Absolute Beginners' (44) and 'The Next Steps' (45) (see page 27).

Available from Maestro Direct, Worldwide Records, Ballroom Dancing Times and other suppliers. (See page 34.)

(73) INSTEP DANCE VIDEOS.

(a)   BEGINNERS' COLLECTION — BALLROOM.

A perfect introduction to the world of ballroom dancing.

4 videos of 60 mins. duration at £17.50 each inclusive.

(i) Social Foxtrot; (ii) Quickstep; (iii) Waltz; (iv) Tango.

(b)   BEGINNERS' COLLECTION — LATIN-AMERICAN.
4 videos of 45 mins. duration. Each £14.50 inclusive.
(i) Rumba; (ii) Cha Cha; (iii) Samba; (iv) Rock Jive.
(c)   MASTER CLASS — BALLROOM.
Designed for people who wish to develop their skills further.
7 videos of 60 mins. duration. Each £17.50 inclusive.
(i) Slow Foxtrot (2); (ii) Quickstep (2); (iii) Waltz (2); (iv) Tango (1).
(d)   MASTER CLASS — LATIN-AMERICAN.
6 videos of 80 mins. duration. Each £17.50 inclusive.
(i) Rumba (2); (ii) Cha Cha Cha (2); (iii) Samba (1); (iv) Jive (1).
Available from Maestro Records. (See page 34.)

(74) IT'S TIME TO DANCE featuring Timothy Howson and Joanne Bolton.
2 videos: (i) Waltz and Quickstep; (ii) Slow Foxtrot, Tango, Rhythm Foxtrot.
Each video £20.00 inclusive.

(75) IT'S TIME TO DANCE featuring Paul Richardson and Lorna Dawson.
2 videos: (a) Cha Cha and Jive; (b) Rumba and Samba.
Each video £20.00 inclusive.
(74) and (75) available from DanceSport International. (See page 21.)

(76) LEARN TO DANCE – MODERN CHV 2042.
Basic steps of the Waltz, Foxtrot, Quickstep and Tango clearly explained and demonstrated by Karen and Marcus Hilton. Introduced by Angela Rippon. £12.99 inclusive.

(77) LET'S GET DANCING – LATIN AMERICAN CVI 2104.
Techniques of the Cha Cha Cha, Samba, Rumba and Paso Doble presented by Sammy Stopford and Barbara McColl. Introduced by Angela Rippon. Suitable for both beginners and more advanced dancers. £12.99 inclusive.
(76) and (77) available from Tema International. (See page 34.)

EXAMINATION-BASED VIDEOS.

(78) IDTA VIDEOS by Guy Howard.

1 Video on Rules and Principles – £59.93.

8 Videos for Associate and Membership for Waltz, Quickstep, Tango and Foxtrot – £50.53 each. (IDTA address on page 21.)

(79) ISTD VIDEOS.

25 videos on ballroom and Latin-American dancing for Licentiate, Associate and Fellowship grades from £29.95 to £47.95 per video. (ISTD address on page 21.)

ORDERING MATERIALS BY POST

Books and videos on sequence dancing are often ordered by post either from specialised suppliers or ballroom associations. A preliminary telephone call is often helpful to find the cost (including postage and packing), whether they will accept credit cards, the wording required on a cheque and any special conditions relating to the sale. Some firms will send a catalogue on request and it may also be possible to negotiate a discount if buying in bulk.

If the exact price is not known one solution is to send an open cheque. This is made out to the supplier, signed and dated but the amount is left blank; it is wise to write a maximum amount at the top of a cheque, e.g. if the estimated price is £8.00 write "max £10". The supplier will fill in the correct amount and state it on his invoice — if the item is out of print the cheque will be returned. Some retailers dislike cheques for small amounts because of bank charges — Brockbank Lane ask for postal orders (not stamps or cheques) for orders of £5 or less.

In most cases items will be delivered within a few days. Associations like IDTA are largely concerned with the needs of their members – purchasers not having a membership number will pay more and delivery may take longer.

BUYING FROM BOOKSELLERS.

Some booksellers specialise in dancing books and videos:–

(a)   Ballroom Dancing Times Bookservice, Clerkenwell House, 45-47 Clerkenwell Green, London, EC1R 0EB.
Tel. 020 7250 3006. Fax 020 7253 6679.

(b)   Dance Books, 15 Cecil Court, London, WC2N 4EZ.
Tel. 020 7836 2314. Fax. 020 7497 0473.

Books, CD's, shoes and other dance products may be obtained from:–

(c)   Dance Sport International Ltd., The Courtyard, Aurelia Road, Croydon, Surrey, CR0 3BF. Tel: 020 8664 8188. Fax: 020 8664 8288. (Sometimes known as Hearn and Spencer.)

An alternative is to place an order with a local bookseller. The delivery period may be weeks rather than days since more stages are involved. To set the process in motion the bookseller has to find the distributor of the item from his data base. Sometimes the title of the book or its author may be sufficient to do this – if not he may ask for the ISBN. The International Standard Book Number is unique to that book. (The ISBN number of this volume is 0-9501927-8-3.) Not all books have ISBN's and some may not appear on the bookseller's computer list.

Databases have improved dramatically in the last few years and most booksellers will print out a list of books on a subject such as sequence dancing or written by a particular author. Lists of contents and other details may be available – even more information is to be found on the Internet.

Dancing books now out of print can often be obtained from second-hand bookshops. It will save time to ask the bookseller before searching the shelves! Two useful web addresses for older books are:–

http://www.booklovers.co.uk
http://www.bibliofind.com

SHOPPING ON THE INTERNET.

Millions of people now purchase items using the Internet – books are one of the most popular products accounting for 40% of sales.

The Internet is an international network of computers linked up to pool information and share facilities. The vast amount of material is classified by web addresses which identify web sites. A web site is a collection of pages produced by someone about a particular subject. Many businesses, booksellers, institutions and suppliers of dancing materials have their own web site. Each site starts with a sort of contents list called the home page followed by information about products and services. A web site of this kind can be seen as an advertisement which can be as lengthy as desired, readily changed and transmitted world-wide at a relatively low cost.

Ordering a book is a fairly simple process for someone with access to a computer linked to the Internet and some basic skills. The first step is to visit the web site of a bookseller by entering an address such as http://www.thebookplace.com. Now locate the book from the home page and click 'add to shopping basket' followed by 'checkout' to bring up a statement. Next click up 'order' to move to a secure web page to enter credit card details and specify the type of delivery required (regular, fast or courier). Finally click 'purchase' and wait for the books to arrive.

Some useful web addresses are:—

Dance Books	http://www.dancebooks.co.uk
Dance Diary	http://www.dancediary.co.uk
DanceSport	http://www.dancesport.uk.com
Dance and Listen Ltd	http://www.danceandlisten.co.uk
IDTA	http://www.idta.co.uk
ISTD	http://www.istd.org
Keytronics	http://www.electricstorm.force 9.co.uk
Portogram	http://www.portogram.co.uk
Westport (UK)	http://www.westport.co.uk

Section II
SEQUENCE DANCING IN THE NINETIES.

INTRODUCTION
The years from 1990 to 1999 have seen the demise of the unofficial sequence dancing organisations, increasing interest in line dancing and the wider spread of information by fax, e-mail and the Internet. There has been no change in the bodies authorised to run official inventive sequence dance competitions and some 45 new dances have appeared each year. The most remarkable year for innovations was 1996 when two mambos, a mazurka and a paso doble were among the winners.

UNOFFICIAL SEQUENCE DANCES
In 1975 the Official Board decreed that all new official dances had to be winners of inventive dance competitions recognised by the Board and dance teachers were discouraged from including other new dances in their programmes. Nevertheless several organisations continued their activities by holding meetings, running dance competitions and circulating journals which often contained scripts of dances arranged by their members – the so-called pirate or Manchester dances. During the nineties membership declined and the societies ceased to exist. These included the Old Time Teachers of Dancing Association (OTTDA); the Sequence Dance Fellowship (SDF London); the Yorkshire Sequence Dance Federation (YSDF) and the National Alliance of Sequence Dancing (NASD). Most of the scripts of these 'unofficial' dances appeared in the journal *'Focus'* edited from 1984 by Ken Fuller of Manchester – this ceased publication in 1995. *'Sequence Dancing World'* (North Star Publishers) is now the only forum for discussion of matters of interest to ordinary sequence dancers.

Further information on these topics is to be found in the *'History of Sequence Dancing and Script List'*, T. A. Whitworth, 1995.

LINE DANCING

Line dancing is a more recent form of sequence in which the dancers do their steps in unison usually all facing in the same direction. It has American roots being often performed in cowboy dress to country - western music. Like modern sequence dancing it has its clubs, textbooks and scripts; there is also a *'Linedance'* magazine published monthly at £2.80 per copy. (Tel: 01704 233154). Although the United Kingdom Alliance (UKA) and International Dance Teachers' Association (IDTA) have introduced syllabuses and medal tests there is as yet no agreed list of official dances – this causes difficulties for line dancers attending sessions in other regions. The overall effect it will have on modern sequence dancing is not clear – it is not a partner dance and it seems to cater for a different age group. In general the sessions are more expensive and this may drive up prices for sequence dancers.

DEVELOPMENTS IN COMMUNICATION

Duplication and distribution of dance scripts has been made much easier by the increasing availability of photocopying devices and the wider use of fax and e-mail. Internet has now become a low-cost method of circulating large quantities of information world-wide. These developments may in due course raise issues relating to copyrights of dance scripts and videos which have never been tested in court.

OFFICIAL INVENTIVE DANCE COMPETITIONS

The bodies authorised to run the official inventive sequence dance competitions from 1990 to 1999 were:–

1. The Official Board of Ballroom Dancing (OBBD); since 1997 the British Dance Council (BDC).
2. Northern Counties Dance Teachers' Association (NCDTA).
3. International Dance Teachers' Association (IDTA).
4. Imperial Society of Teachers of Dancing (ISTD).
5. Allied Dancing Association (ADA).
6. United Kingdom Alliance (UKA or UKAPTD).

46

7.   British Association of Teachers of Dancing (BATD).
8.   Scottish Dance Teachers' Association (SDTA).
9.   National Association of Teachers of Dancing (NATD).
10.   International Sequence Dance Circle (ISDC).
11/12. Butlins (Bognor Regis and Pwllheli).
13.   Blackpool Tower Company (Blackpool).
14.   'Dance News' Magazine (Slough).
15.   David Bullen Enterprises (North of Britain).

Nos. 1–9 derive their authority from being members of the Official Board. Not all the competitions are 'open' in the sense that some associations restrict entry to their own members.

Competitions in the three sections are not always held at the same venue at the same time, e.g. in 1994 the UKA held the modern competition at Weston Super Mare in February and the O/T and Latin-American sections at Blackpool in June.

TOO MANY NEW DANCES!

A common complaint among sequence dancers is that there are too many new dances. This view is often expressed by those who wish to dance less frequently and good dancers whose health is declining. With this in mind the Sequence Faculty Committee of the ISTD has decided to reduce the number of new dances in 2000 by one by adopting a rotational system for the three sections. Competitions will be held for ballroom and classical sections but not for the Latin American. A more recent event has been the cancellation of the three North of Britain competitions — this will further reduce the number of new dances to 41 for the year 2000.

Another important issue is the spacing of the inventive dance competitions throughout the year. In the year 2000 there will be no new dances in March and December but 9 between the 27th August and the 16th of September! This problem can only be solved by some give-and-take between the various organisers – the powers of the British Dance Council are limited in these areas.

47

NEW OFFICIAL DANCES 1990 – 1999

Tango	74	Blues	13
Rumba	61	Samba	7
Mod Waltz	59	O/T Waltz	6
Saunter	45	Mambo	6
Cha Cha Cha	44	Two Step	3
Foxtrot	37	Bossa Nova	3
Quickstep	30	Paso Doble	1
Jive	28	Mazurka	1
Swing	17	TOTAL	450
Gavotte	15		

Two winners from Ireland's East Coast Classic competition did not gain recognition from the Official Board and are not included in the lists – the Granby Waltz (1991) by Flora Millar and the Studio Samba (1992) by Jeff and Muriel Aldren.

A surprise in the list is to see 6 sequence mambos since the last prize winner was Jan Telford's Mambo Italiano of 1955. (This was inspired by the song of the same name often sung by Rosemary Clooney).

The mambo may be seen as a faster version of the rumba; it has a basic rhythm of quick, quick, slow often danced as step, step, hold. The Mambo Magic (1996) dances well to the country-western Hillbilly Rock of the Woolpackers – it makes a good party dance. The mambo, salsa, merengue, and other Latin dances are popular with ballroom dancers in London and the South East. Two sequence salsas were entered for the UKA dance competition in January 1999.

Graham and Kathy Thomson's Princess Mazurka of 1996 was the first winner for this type of dance since the Columbine Mazurka of Ted Burroughs in 1976. Mazurkas are danced to music in 3/4 time like waltzes but the accent is placed on the second beat giving an unusual and attractive rhythm. The characteristic figure for the dance is a peculiar hopping step called the pas de mazurka.

The Paso Petite arranged by Rachael Wadey, was also a winner in 1996 – the first since the Pepi Paso of 1986 by Annette Sheridan and Ray Reeves.

THE DANCES OF THE NINETIES

The winning dances for the years 1990 to 1999 appear on the following pages. Dances from the Victorian era to 1994 are set out in the same format in the *'History of Sequence Dancing and Script List'*. T. A. Whitworth 1995.

The dances are placed in alphabetical order. Where the name of the dance comes first as in the Tango Serida and Saunter Together this written as Serida [Tango] and Together [Saunter]. The names in the list are the arrangers and in most cases the performers of the winning sequence dances.

A winning dance in a class should be the best arrangement of steps bearing in mind such factors as technical merit, flow and general suitability for average sequence dancers. The final selection will however often be influenced by style of performance, the music chosen, the fame of the competitors and other imponderables.

LEADING ARRANGERS 1990 – 1999.

Graham & Kathy Thomson	33
Ian & Sue Webster	30
Philip Ainsley & Lorraine Heron	25
Graham & Avril Watkins	21
Don Millington & June Macready	18
Michael & Angela Hayton	16
David Howker	14
Neil & Lesley Marshall	14
Howard & Joan Cookson	13
⎡ Michael & Ann Morris	12
Michael Morris with other partners	6
⎣ Ann Morris with other partners	5

Couples winning all three sections were:–

David Howker & Michelle Webster	(ISTD March 1998)
David Hipshaw & Pauline Griffiths	(ADA May 1996)
Neil & Lesley Marshall	(ADA May 1998)

Presented in 1990

Waltzes (Old Time) (1990)
Galaxy	Mark Paton & Jacquie Davis	Dance News

Waltzes (Modern) (1990)
Callam's	Graham & Kathy Thomson	IDTA
Omega	David Howker & Elizabeth Atkinson	North of Britain
Sheridan	Audrey Bromage & Michelle Webster	NATD
Wensley	Philip Ainsley & Lorraine Heron	BCBD
Westlynn	Howard & Joan Cookson	BATD
Wetheral	Michael & Angela Hayton	Butlins Pwllheli

Tangos (1990)
Debonaire [Tango] (Mod)	Ken & Barbara Street	ISTD
Edor [Tango] (O/T)	Edgar & Doris Holroyd	NCDTA
Nadine [Tango] (O/T)	Philip Ainsley & Lorraine Heron	UKAPTD
Newfield (Mod)	Michael & Angela Hayton	SDTA
Tony (O/T)	Jim & Madge Curley	SDTA
Vilamoura [Tango] (O/T)	Michael & Angela Hayton	Butlins Pwllheli

Cha Cha Chas (1990)
Carley	Michael & Ann Morris	ISDC
Chilli	Albert & Florence Clark	NCTDA
Chinchilla	Graham Crookes & Doreen Wareing	STDA
Continental	Nicola Twigg & David Barrett	IDTA
Corrida	Michael & Ann Morris	ADA
Sarah's	Audrey Bromage & Michelle Webster	NATD

Rumbas (1990)
Charlene [Rumba]	Philip Ainsley & Lorraine Heron	North of Britain
Delight [Rumba]	Patricia Jay & Gary Fleetwood	Butlins Bognor Regis
Dominique [Rumba]	David Bullen & Iverna Corcoran	Blackpool
Poldhu	Audrey & Allan Bainbridge	BATD
Sabor [Rumba]	Graham Crookes & Doreen Wareing	UKAPTD

Saunters (1990)
Bel-Air [Saunter]	Michael & Ann Morris	ADA
Kingfisher	Graham & Kathy Thomson	Blackpool
Kirsty	Howard & Joanne Cookson	BATD
Samara [Saunter]	Philip Ainsley & Lorraine Heron	North of Britain

Foxtrots (1990)

Felicity	Albert & Florence Clark	NCDTA
Fortuna	Mark Paton & Jacquie Davis	Dance News
Harlequin	Ken & Barbara Street	Butlins Bognor Regis
Nevada	David Howker & Elizabeth Atkinson	ISDC

Quicksteps (1990)

Appleby	Jeff & Muriel Aldren	ADA
Chandella	Philip Ainsley & Lorraine Heron	UKAPTD
Margie	Jim & Madge Curley	Blackpool

Gavottes (1990)

Gwendoline	Ken & Barbara Street	Butlins Bognor Regis
Regency	Nicola Twigg & David Barrett	NATD
Sunset	Barry & Julie Earnshaw	BCBD

Jives (1990)

Alphabet	Steve & Diane Shaw	Dance News
Jetta	Graham Crookes & Doreen Wareing	BCBD
Shelley	Audrey Bromage & Michelle Webster	ISTD

Swings (1990)

Savana	Graham Crookes & Doreen Wareing	ISDC
Sharron	Ken & Barbara Street	IDTA

Blues (1990)

Berkeley	Peter Sharpe	ISTD

Sambas (1990)

Marina [Samba]	Michael & Ann Morris	Butlins Pwllheli

Leading Arrangers (1990)

5 – Philip Ainsley & Lorraine Heron   2 – Howard & Joanne Cookson
4 – Graham Crookes & Doreen Wareing 2 – Jim & Madge Curley
4 – Michael & Ann Morris   2 – David Howker & Elizabeth Atkinson
4 – Ken & Barbara Street   2 – Mark Paton & Jacquie Davis
3 – Audrey Bromage & Michelle Webster 2 – Graham & Kathy Thomson
3 – Michael & Angela Hayton   2 – Nicola Twigg & David Barrett
2 – Albert & Florence Clark

Presented in 1991

Waltzes (Modern) (1991)

Bellerby	Philip Ainsley & Lorraine Heron	Blackpool
Blue Dawn	Mary Cruickshank	ISTD
Blue Lace	Ken & Barbara Street	IDTA
Claudia's	Graham & Kathy Thomson	North of Britain
Clinique [Waltz]	David Hipshaw & Pauline Griffiths	ADA
Washington	Mark Paton & Jacquie Davis	Slough

Tangos (1991)

Glendale (Mod)	Graham & Kathy Thomson	BCBD
Mirage (O/T)	Barry & Julie Earnshaw	North of Britain
Taurus (O/T)	Mark Paton & Jacquie Davis	Slough
Torque (Mod)	Albert & Florence Clark	NCDTA
Tripoli (O/T)	Philip Ainsley & Lorraine Heron	NCDTA
Tuscany (O/T)	Audrey Bromage & Ron Lane	NATD

Saunters (1991)

Carousel	Howard & Joanne Cookson	Blackpool
Columbine	Ken & Barbara Street	ISDC
Feline [Saunter]	Ken & Enid Smith	Butlins Bognor Regis
Princess	Michael & Ann Morris	ADA
Redrose	Steven & Diane Shaw	Butlins Pwllheli
Sateen [Saunter]	Robert & Kathleen Pickering	ISTD

Rumbas (1991)

Lakeside	Barry & Julie Earnshaw	Butlins Pwllheli
Louise [Rumba]	Graham & Kathy Thomson	BCBD
Riverdale	Sid & Shirley Robson	NCDTA
Rosemount	Philip Ainsley & Lorraine Heron	Blackpool
Ruskin	Andrew Pigg & Doreen Wareing	Slough

Cha Cha Chas (1991)

Anitra	Alwyn Leathley & Elsie Platts	IDTA
Claymore	Graham & Kathy Thomson	SDTA
Clio	David Hipshaw & Pauline Griffiths	ADA
Dominion	Mary Cruickshank	ISTD
Susie Q	Arthur & Jean Parr	North of Britain

Jives (1991)

Bee Hive	John & Jean Moody	ISDC
Disney	David Barrett & Nicola Twigg	NATD
Jimpy	Reg & Sylvia Dart	Butlins Bognor Regis
Joplin	Ray Bulpitt & Doreen Wareing	UKA

Foxtrots (1991)

Grosvenor	Muriel Aldren	Butlins Pwllheli
Nicola	Norman & Linda Briggs	Butlins Bognor Regis
Sahara	Audrey Bromage & Ron Lane	NATD
White Heather	Graham & Kathy Thomson	SDTA

Quicksteps (1991)

Kay's	Jim & Madge Curley	BATD
Quatro	Graham Crookes & Doreen Wareing	ISDC
Roxy	David Howker & Elizabeth Atkinson	UKA

Swings (1991)

Sacha	Michael & Ann Morris	UKA
Sandown	Howard & Joanne Cookson	BATD

Gavottes (1991)

Primrose	Patricia Jay & Gary Fleetwood	IDTA
Shimmering	Graham & Kathy Thomson	SDTA

Sambas (1991)

Popcorn	Audrey & Allan Bainbridge	BATD

Two Step (1991)

Solara	Mike & Sheree Savory	BCBD

Leading Arrangers (1991)

6 – Graham & Kathy Thomson
3 – Philip Ainsley & Lorraine Heron
2 – Audrey Bromage & Ron Lane
2 – Howard & Joanne Cookson
2 – Mary Cruickshank

2 – Barry & Julie Earnshaw
2 – David Hipshaw & Pauline Griffiths
2 – Michael & Ann Morris
2 – Mark Paton & Jacquie Davis
2 – Ken & Barbara Street

Presented in 1992

Waltzes (Modern) (1992)

Apple Blossom	Samantha Haywood	ISTD
Border	Michael & Angela Hayton	SDTA
Chambellan [Waltz]	Philip Ainsley & Lorraine Heron	Blackpool
Denverdale	Steven & Diane Shaw	Butlins Pwllheli
Hadrians	Michael & Angela Hayton	UKA
Highfield	Steven & Diane Shaw	Slough
Rabanne [Waltz]	Elsie Platts & Alwyn Leathley	ISDC

Tangos (1992)

Leanne [Tango] (O/T)	Philip Ainsley & Lorraine Heron	UKA
Negro [Tango] (O/T)	Don & Jan Nicholson	NCDTA
Nightfire (O/T)	Ian & Sue Webster	ISDC
Telecon (Mod)	Alwyn Leathley	ADA
Tornado (O/T)	Ted & Sue Burroughs	Blackpool
Torviscas [Tango] (O/T)	Philip Ainsley & Lorraine Heron	BCBD
Trafalgar (O/T)	Michael & Ann Morris	ADA

Rumbas (1992)

Atlanta [Rumba]	Elizabeth Atkinson & Paul Wallace	ISDC
Fantasia [Rumba]	Graham & Kathy Thomson	North of Britain
Noir [Rumba]	Pat Sharkey & Yvonne White	SDTA
Pineapple	Michael Beetham	UKA
Rafika [Rumba]	Colin Taylor & Carol Thirlaway	NCDTA
Regency	Ted & Sue Burroughs	BATD
Renaissance	Audrey Bromage & Ron Lane	ISTD
Richard's	Flora Millar	Blackpool

Saunters (1992)

Centenary	Jim & Madge Curley	BATD
Cerise	Graham & Avril Watkins	Butlins Bognor Regis
Sandringham	John & Maureen Dack	Slough
Shakara [Saunter]	Graham & Kathy Thomson	North of Britain
Solazur [Saunter]	Philip Ainsley & Lorraine Heron	BCBD
St. Clair [Saunter]	Michael & Ann Morris	SDTA

Quicksteps (1992)

Florentine	Graham & Kathy Thomson	North of Britain
Katrina	Joanne & Howard Cookson	BATD
Quality	Ted & Sue Burroughs	NATD
Queslett	Mark Paton & Jacquie Davis	IDTA

Cha Cha Chas (1992)

CJ	Clive & Jennifer Hurt	Butlins Bognor Regis
Commador	Michael & Ann Morris	ADA
Ebony	Ian & Sue Webster	Butlins Pwllheli
Mahogany	Ian & Sue Webster	Slough

Foxtrots (1992)

April	Graham & Avril Watkins	Butlins Bognor Regis
Tempro	Margaret Halliday	NCDTA

Swings (1992)

Linden	Ken & Barbara Street	ISTD
Singapore	Theo & Doreen Ball	IDTA

Sambas (1992)

Social	Pat Sharkey & Yvonne White	IDTA

Bossa Novas (1992)

Bella	June Macready & Don Millington	NATD

Blues (1992)

Cheney	Patricia Jay & Gary Fleetwood	Butlins Pwllheli

Jives (1992)

Jessica	Eric & Jean Taylor	BCBD

Gavottes (1992)

Lladro	Jeff & Muriel Aldren	NATD

Leading Arrangers (1992)

4 – Philip Ainsley & Lorraine Heron	2 – Michael & Angela Hayton
3 – Graham & Kathy Thomson	2 – Steven & Diane Shaw
3 – Ted & Sue Burroughs	2 – Graham & Avril Watkins
3 – Michael & Ann Morris	2 – Pat Sharkey & Yvonne White
3 – Ian & Sue Webster	

Presented in 1993

Waltzes (Modern) (1993)

Carliol	Michael & Angela Hayton	Butlins Pwllheli
Cerise [Waltz]	Michael Beetham & Doreen Wareing	ADA
Lovely Lady	Steve & Kathleen Wright	ISDC
Sophie's	Graham & Kathy Thomson	IDTA
Windsor	Stuart & Karen Wright	Blackpool

Tangos (1993)

Danielle [Tango] (Mod)	Don Millington & June Macready	NATD
Gibson (O/T)	Stuart & Karen Wright	Blackpool
Merrick (Mod)	Bob & Veronica Ryan	ISTD
Nocturne [Tango] (O/T)	Don Millington & June Macready	Slough
Renoir [Tango] (O/T)	Pat Sharkey & Yvonne White	ISDC
Samarnie (O/T)	Neil & Leslie Marshall	SDTA
Tanya (Mod)	Paul Wallace	BATD
Thirlmere (O/T)	Michael & Angela Hayton	Butlins Pwllheli
Troodos (O/T)	Howard & Joanne Cookson	BATD
Turnberry (O/T)	Philip Ainsley & Lorraine Heron	North of Britain
Vienna [Tango] (Mod)	Graham & Kathy Thomson	BCBD

Rumbas (1993)

Apollo [Rumba]	Paul Wallace & Elizabeth Atkinson	Butlins Pwllheli
Invicta	Bill & Gay Pugh	UKA
Miami	Audrey Bromage and Ron Lane	ISTD
Raynham	Philip Ainsley & Lorraine Heron	North of Britain
Venezia [Rumba]	Philip Ainsley & Lorraine Heron	Blackpool

Cha Cha Chas (1993)

Charlies	Dorothy Hudson & Jean Taylor	ADA
Katie	Michelle Webster & David Howker	NATD
Mario	Graham & Avril Watkins	Butlins Bognor Regis
Rachel	Margaret & Edwin Halliday	IDTA
Waikiki	Paul Wallace	BATD

Saunters (1993)

Azalia	Dorothy Hudson & Jean Taylor	ADA
Melrose	David & Ann Lavery	Slough
Oxbury	Michelle Webster & David Howker	NATD
Romero [Saunter]	Patricia Jay & Gary Fleetwood	UKA

Jives (1993)

Jambo	Colin Taylor & Carol Thirlaway	SDTA
Julie's	Margaret & Edwin Halliday	NCDTA
Jurassic	Roy & Jean Hopkinson	Slough
Let's	Ray & Bridget Fenton-Storey	BCBD

Foxtrot (1993)

Jasmine	David Belshaw & Karen Kelly	NCDTA
Philishar	Jim & Madge Curley	SDTA
Stardust	Graham & Avril Watkins	Butlins Bognor Regis

Quicksteps (1993)

Katy	Ross & Shirley Hillman	North of Britain
Richmond	Michael Beetham & Doreen Wareing	UKA

Swings (1993)

Chevy	Colin Taylor & Carol Thirlaway	NCDTA
Ivory	Patricia Jay & Gary Fleetwood	IDTA

Miscellaneous (1993)

Grenadier Two Step	Ken & Barbara Street	ISTD
Scirocco Samba	Roy & Jean Hopkinson	ISDC
Starlight Gavotte	Maureen & John Dack	Butlins Bognor Regis
Stephanne Blues	Pat Sharkey & Yvonne White	BCBD

Leading Arrangers

3 – Philip Ainsley & Lorraine Heron
3 – Paul Wallace
2 – Michael Beetham & Doreen Wareing
2 – Margaret & Edwin Halliday
2 – Michael & Angela Hayton
2 – Roy & Jean Hopkinson
2 – Dorothy Hudson & Jean Taylor
2 – Patricia Jay & Gary Fleetwood

2 – Don Millington & June Macready
2 – Pat Sharkey & Yvonne White
2 – Colin Taylor & Carol Thirlaway
2 – Graham & Kathy Thomson
2 – Graham & Avril Watkins
2 – Michelle Webster & David Howker
2 – Stuart & Karen Wright

Presented in 1994

Waltzes (Old-Time) (1994)

Sovereign	John & Maureen Dack	UKA
Waltz of Vienna	Jeff & Muriel Aldren	SDTA
Wednesday	Rachel Wadey	ISTD

Waltzes (Modern) (1994)

Aurora	Michelle Webster & David Howker	ISTD
Centenary	Malcolm T. Brister (Ann Green)	Blackpool
Parkgate	Jeff & Muriel Aldren	Butlins Pwllheli
Springside	Howard & Joanne Cookson	BATD
Stacey Ann	Neil & Lesley Marshall	SDTA

Tangos (1994)

Blackpool Tower (Mod)	Arthur & Jean Parr	IDTA
Cassanova [Tg] (Mod)	Don Millington & June Macready	NATD
Devoran (O/T)	Michael & Ann Morris	Slough
Heartbeat (O/T)	Graham & Avril Watkins	IDTA
Lanercost (O/T)	Michael & Angela Hayton	Butlins Pwllheli
Moderato [Tango] (Mod)	Margaret Yates & Carol Parry	ADA
Teak (O/T)	Ian & Sue Webster	Blackpool
Trevini (O/T)	Philip Ainsley & Lorraine Heron	North Of Britain

Rumbas (1994)

Caprice [Rumba]	Ken & Barbara Street	ISTD
Cosmopolitan	David Howker & Michelle Webster	NATD
Dorice [Rumba]	David Bullen & Iverna Corcoran	BCBD
Elise [Rumba]	Graham & Kathy Thomson	Blackpool
Headlands	Audrey & Allan Bainbridge	BATD
Raquel [Rumba]	Bob & Diane Smith	ADA
Rosewood	Ian & Sue Webster	ISDC
Samantha [Rumba]	Lesley Hawthorne	IDTA
Tamara [Rumba]	Ian & Sue Webster	NCDTA

Foxtrots (1994)

Cheslyn	Terry & Ethel Grundy	Slough
Emerald	Graham & Avril Watkins	Butlins Bognor Regis
Maple	Ian & Sue Webster	NCDTA
Mirror Glass	Malcolm Brister (Ann Green)	BCBD

Saunters (1994)

Navidia	June Day & Deborah Long	BATD
Sandalwood	Ian & Sue Webster	ISDC
Sonata [Saunter]	Bob & Diane Smith	ADA
Sovereign	Ian & Sue Webster	NCDTA

Cha Cha Chas (1994)

Caroland	Andrew Pigg & Caroline Roberts	Butlins Pwllheli
Par [Cha Cha]	Arthur & Jean Parr	North of Britain
Paradise	Roy Randall & Heather Pitman	Slough

Quicksteps (1994)

Bernena	Neil & Lesley Marshall	ISDC
Somerset	Malcolm Brister (Ann Green)	UKA
Trojan	David Howker & Michelle Webster	North of Britain

Jives (1994)

Coca Rola	Arthur & Jean Parr	UKA
Jennie	Michael & Ann Morris	SDTA

Blues (1994)

Aqua	Graham & Avril Watkins	BCBD

Gavottes (1994)

Charlotte	John & Maureen Dack	Butlins Bognor Regis

Sambas (1994)

Miami	Steven & Diane Shaw	Butlins Bognor Regis

Swings (1994)

Shamrock	David Trowbridge & Beverley Crowder	NATD

Leading Arrangers (1994)

6 – Ian & Sue Webster	2 – Jeff & Muriel Aldren
3 – Malcolm Brister	2 – John and Maureen Dack
3 – David Howker & Michelle Webster	2 – Neil & Lesley Marshall
3 – Arthur & Jean Parr	2 – Michael & Ann Morris
3 – Graham & Avril Watkins	2 – Bob & Diane Smith

Presented in 1995

Waltzes (Old-Time) (1995)

Countess	Robert & Louise Aldred	BCBD

Waltzes (Modern) (1995)

Hannah's	Margaret & Edwin Halliday	Slough
Oriana	John & Maureen Dack	Butlins Bognor Regis
Pearl	Barry Jones & Elaine Starkey	UKA
Pendle	Howard & Joanne Cookson	BATD
Royle	Jeff & Muriel Aldren	North of Britain
Westbury	Philip Ainsley & Lorraine Heron	NCDTA

Tangos (1995)

Gerald's (O/T)	Roy Randall & Heather Pitman	Slough
Italia [Tango] (Mod)	Don Millington & June Macready	Butlins Pwllheli
Kouros (O/T)	Elsie Platts & Alwyn Leathley	ADA
Orlando [Tango] (O/T)	Andrew Pigg & Caroline Roberts	North of Britain
Terrifique [Tango] (Mod)	Don Millington & June Macready	NATD
Tigra (O/T)	Lorraine Heron & Philip Ainsley	NCDTA

Rumbas (1995)

Continental	George McDonald & Kyla Bellinghall	ADA
Deargo [Rumba]	David Howker & Michelle Webster	NATD
Leon	Michelle Webster & David Howker	ISTD
Marietta [Rumba]	Paul & Susan Wallace	BATD
Quizas? [Rumba}	Darren Park & Andrea Kilgour	Blackpool
Radiant	Shirley & Sid Robson	NCDTA
Rosamar [Rumba]	Arthur & Jean Parr	IDTA

Foxtrots (1995)

Acacia	Graham & Kathy Thomson	BCBD
Derwent	Michael & Angela Hayton	ISDC
Fantasia	Alwyn Leathley & Elsie Platts	ADA
Four Winds	Arthur & Jean Parr	IDTA

Cha Cha Chas (1995)

Colimar	Madge & Tony Curley	SDTA
Kariokee	Ted & Sue Burroughs	Butlins Bognor Regis
Niki Noo	Graham & Avril Watkins	Butlins Pwllheli
Rosamar	Arthur & Jean Parr	UKA
Whiskey	Ann Morris & Freda Nizinkiewicz	ISDC

Saunters (1995)

Contara [Saunter]	June Day	BATD
Shola	Mark Paton & Jacquie Davis	Blackpool
Simplicity	Don Millington & Joan Macready	UKA
Valentine	Graham & Avril Watkins	IDTA

Blues (1995)

Ballerina	Ted & Sue Burroughs	Butlins Bognor Regis
Bernstan	Neil & Leslie Marshall	SDTA
Bertie's	David Howker & Michelle Webster	NATD

Quicksteps (1995)

Carousel	Paul & Susan Wallace	SDTA
Cyprio	Michelle Webster & David Howker	ISTD
Kareen	Andrew Pigg & Audrey Bromage	Blackpool

Swings (1995)

Ryans	Neil & Lesley Marshall	ISDC
Safron	Andrew Pigg & Caroline Roberts	Butlins Pwllheli

Miscellaneous

Blighty Bossa Nova	Don Millington & June Macready	Slough
Boogie Jive	Michael & Ann Morris	North of Britain
Poirot Gavotte	Michelle Webster & David Howker	ISTD
Susie Samba	Paul & Susan Wallace	BCBD

Leading Arrangers (1995)

5 – David Howker & Michelle Webster	2 – Philip Ainsley & Lorraine Heron
4 – Don Millington & June Macready	2 – Ted & Sue Burroughs
3 – Arthur & Jean Parr	2 – Alwyn Leathley & Elsie Platts
3 – Andrew Pigg & Caroline Roberts	2 – Neil & Lesley Marshall
3 – Paul & Susan Wallace	2 – Graham & Avril Watkins

Presented in 1996

Waltzes (Modern) (1996)

Charlotte's	Graham & Kathy Thomson	North of Britain
Elizabeth's	Darren Badder & Hilary Biggs	SDTA
Indigo [Waltz]	David Hipshaw & Pauline Griffiths	ADA
Mayfield	Kevin Page & Valerie Laws	NATD
Victoria Ann [Waltz]	Deborah Long (Renee Turner)	BATD
Waverley	Ron & Susan Fulham	UKA

Tangos (1996)

Classique [Tango] (Mod)	Graham & Kathy Thomson	BCBD
Eden Valley (Mod)	Michael & Angela Hayton	IDTA
Lakeland (O/T)	Michael & Angela Hayton	UKA
Munro [Tango] (O/T)	David Hipshaw & Pauline Griffiths	ADA
Tartan (O/T)	Graham & Kathy Thomson	SDTA
Tea Dance (O/T)	Darren Badder & Hilary Biggs	North of Britain
Tonite [Tango] (O/T)	Darren Park & Sharon McCann	Blackpool
Totara [Tango] (O/T)	Ian & Susan Webster	NCDTA
Trésor [Tango] (O/T)	Graham & Avril Watkins	IDTA

Rumbas (1996)

Miranda [Rumba]	David Hipshaw & Pauline Griffiths	ADA
Redwood	Graham & Avril Watkins	BCBD
Reno	Sid & Shirley Robson	NCDTA
Sapele	Ian & Sue Webster	ISDC

Foxtrots (1996)

Amethyst	Graham & Kathy Thomson	Blackpool
Diamond Jubilee	Sue & Ian Webster	Butlins Bognor Regis
Ennerdale	Michael & Angela Hayton	ISDC
Fragrance	Graham & Avril Watkins	Butlins Pwllheli

Quicksteps (1996)

Cassie	Graham & Kathy Thomson	Slough
Coromandel	Ian & Sue Webster	NCDTA
Libra	David Howker & Michelle Webster	ISTD

Cha Cha Chas (1996)

Cracker Barrel	Arthur & Jean Parr	North of Britain
Diamond Jubilee	David & Ann Lavery	Butlins Bognor Regis
D.J.	Dorothy Hudson & Jean Taylor	UKA
Empress	Shelagh Buckley & Malcolm Brister	IDTA

Jives (1996)

Bucks Fizz	Michael Morris & Beverley Berry	SDTA
Cosmic	Malcolm Brister & Shelagh Buckley	Blackpool
Gemma Lou	Arthur & Jean Parr	Butlins Pwllheli

Blues (1996)

Banyan	Ian & Sue Webster	Slough
Boyden	Graham & Avril Watkins	Butlins Pwllheli

Mambos (1996)

Magic [Mambo]	Don Millington & June Macready	Slough
Pain	Audrey & Alan Bainbridge	BATD

Two Steps (1996)

Diamond Jubilee	Rachel Wadey	Butlins Bognor Regis

Miscellaneous (1996)

Bossa Nova Brazil	Don Millington & June Macready	NATD
Emerald Gavotte	S. Haywood & A. Staley	ISTD
Gatsby Swing	Michael Morris & Beverley Berry	ISDC
Paso Petite	Rachel Wadey	ISTD
Princess Mazurka	Graham & Kathy Thomson	BCBD
Salou [Saunter]	Howard & Joanne Cookson	BATD
West [Swing]	Kevin Page & Valerie Laws	NATD

Leading Arrangers (1996)

6 – Graham & Kathy Thomson	2 – Malcolm Brister & Shelagh Buckley
5 – Ian & Sue Webster	2 – Don Millington & June Macready
4 – Graham & Avril Watkins	2 – Michael Morris & Beverley Berry
3 – Michael & Angela Hayton	2 – Kevin Page & Valerie Laws
3 – David Hipshaw & Pauline Griffiths	2 – Arthur & Jean Parr
2 – Darren Badder & Hilary Biggs	2 – Rachel Wadey

Presented in 1997

Waltzes (Old-Time) (1997)

Whinlatter	Michael & Angela Hayton	SDTA

Waltzes (Modern) (1997)

Arcadia	John & Maureen Dack	NATD
Bessie's	Philip & Helen Blackburn	North of Britain
Caribbean	Michael Pharaoh & Julie Williams	Butlins Bognor Regis
Garwood	Paul & Susan Wallace	BATD
Jason's	Graham & Kathy Thomson	SDTA
Lara's	Robert & Louise Aldred	ISDC
Westovian	Jim & Hazel Wake	ISTD

Tangos (1997)

Cape Town (O/T)	Don Millington & June Macready	NATD
Natal [Tango] (O/T)	Don Millington & June Macready	ADA
Sixteen [Tango] (O/T)	Howard & Joanne Cookson	BATD
Tamarisk (Mod)	Ian & Sue Webster	UKA
Tenacity (O/T)	Philip & Helen Blackburn	Blackpool
Trent (Mod)	Graham & Kathy Thomson	BDC
Yew Tree (O/T)	Ian & Sue Webster	Butlins Bognor Regis

Rumbas (1997)

Eden Vale	Michael & Angela Hayton	North of Britain
Queen of Hearts	Audrey Bromage (Michelle Webster)	NATD
Raspberry	Jacqueline Naylor & V. Burnett	ISTD
Rossley	Graham & Kathy Thomson	UKA
Roxanne [Rumba]	David Belshaw & Karen Kelly	NCDTA

Saunters (1997)

Cedar	Ian & Sue Webster	NCDTA
Snowdrop	Graham & Kathy Thomson	North of Britain
Strangward	Darren Badder & Hilary Biggs	Butlins Pwllheli
Sunflower	Graham & Avril Watkins	ISDC

Cha Cha Chas (1997)

Beyzabanu	Colin Piper	Butlins Bognor Regis
Christiana	Paul & Susan Wallace	BATD
Zanzibar	Philip & Helen Blackburn	Blackpool

Jives (1997)

CK	Roy & Jean Hopkinson	Slough
Honkeytonk	Peter Nuttall & Ann Morris	Butlins Pwllheli
Jackpot	Michael Morris & Beverley Berry	ISDC
Jean's	Arthur & Jean Parr	IDTA
Kandy	Colin Taylor & Carol Thurlaway	SDTA

Foxtrots (1997)

Eternity	Graham & Kathy Thomson	Slough
Passionata	Philip & Helen Blackburn	Butlins Pwllheli
Springtime	Ann Morris & Peter Nuttall	ADA

Gavottes (1997)

Classical Grey	Darren Badder & Hilary Biggs	BDC
Golden	Graham & Avril Watkins	Slough
Romany	J. Sanderson & M. Habergham	ISTD

Quicksteps (1997)

Kelly	Andrew Pigg & Caroline Roberts	Blackpool
Keresley	Colin Taylor & Carol Thirlaway	NCTDA
Quintonian	Neil & Lesley Marshall	IDTA

Swings (1997)

Abbey	Peter Nuttall & Ann Morris	UKA
Astral	Malcolm Brister & Shelagh Buckley	IDTA

Mambos (1997)

Hey	Philip & Helen Blackburn	BDC
Mia [Mambo]	Don Millington & June Macready	ADA

Leading Arrangers (1997)

5 – Philip & Helen Blackburn	2 – Darren Badder & Hilary Biggs
5 – Graham & Kathy Thomson	2 – Michael & Angela Hayton
3 – Don Millington & June Macready	2 – Colin Taylor & Carol Thirlaway
3 – Peter Nuttall & Ann Morris	2 – Paul & Susan Wallace
3 – Ian & Sue Webster	2 – Graham & Avril Watkins

Presented in 1998

Waltzes (Modern) (1998)

Constance	Don Millington & June Macready	NATD
Kopaz	Darren Park & Andrea Kilgour	Blackpool
Rachel's	Howard & Joanne Cookson	BATD
Watermill	Philip Ainsley & Lorraine Heron	NCDTA
Willow Wood	Ian & Sue Webster	Butlins Pwllheli

Tangos (1998)

Antigua [Tango] (O/T)	Michael Pharaoh & Julie Williams	Slough
Bernini [Tango] (O/T)	Neil & Lesley Marshall	ADA
Emreco [Tango] (O/T)	Philip Ainsley & Lorraine Heron	NCDTA
Glencroft (Mod)	Graham & Kathy Thomson	SDTA
Margeriten (Mod)	Neil & Leslie Marshall	ADA
Tara (O/T)	Philip Ainsley & Lorraine Heron	Blackpool
Tango 44 (O/T)	Tracy Mason & George Fildes	BDC

Saunters (1998)

Finesse [Saunter]	David Howker & Michelle Webster	NATD
Saville [Saunter]	Peter Nuttall & Ann Morris	Butlins Pwllheli
Seraya [Saunter]	Ian & Sue Webster	IDTA
Sheldan	June Day & Robin Flynn	BATD
Sinatra [Saunter]	Philip & Helen Blackburn	UKA
Summer-Wind	Philip Ainsley & Lorraine Heron	North of Britain

Rumbas (1998)

Millennium	Graham & Kathy Thomson	UKA
Parisienne	Graham & Kathy Thomson	SDTA
Red Rose	Barbara & Harry Howarth	ISDC
Red Velvet	Graham & Avril Watkins	Slough
Rembrant	Philip Ainsley & Lorraine Heron	NCDTA
Resolution	Kevin Page & Valerie Laws	NATD
Ritzy	Paul & Susan Wallace	BATD
Rowan	Ian & Sue Webster	Butlins Bognor Regis

Quicksteps (1998)

Conomara	Philip Ainsley & Lorraine Heron	North of Britain
Elderberry	Ian & Sue Webster	Slough
Keaki	Ian & Sue Webster	IDTA

Foxtrots (1998)

Albany	Robert & Louise Aldred	ISTD
Coniston	Michael & Angela Hayton	ISDC
Gardenia	Ian & Sue Webster	UKA
Jessica's	Philip Ainsley & Lorraine Heron	BDC
Sea Breeze	Michael Pharaoh & Julie Williams	Butlins Bognor Regis

Cha Cha Chas (1988)

Canasta	Neil & Lesley Marshall	ADA
Capice [Cha Cha]	Darren & Elaine Park	North of Britain
Cocobola	Ian & Sue Webster	Blackpool
Issy	Mark Paton & Jacquie Davies	BDC

Blues (1998)

Brandy	Graham & Kathy Thomson	ISTD
September	Neil & Leslie Marshall	SDTA

Jive

Blackjack	Michael Morris & Beverley Berry	Butlins Pwllheli

Swing

Gin	Michael Morris & Beverley Berry	ISDC

Gavotte

Golden Oak	Ian & Sue Webster	Butlins Bognor Regis

Mambo

Mystique	Graham & Avril Watkins	ISTD

Samba

Sizzlers	Arthur & Jean Parr	IDTA

Leading Arrangers (1998)

8 – Ian & Sue Webster

7 – Philip Ainsley & Lorraine Heron

4 – Neil & Lesley Marshall

4 – Graham & Kathy Thomson

2 – Michael Morris & Beverley Berry

2 – Michael Pharaoh & Julie Williams

2 – Graham & Avril Watkins

Presented in 1999

Waltzes (Modern) (1999)

Dawn's	Don & June Millington	Slough
Millennium	Graham & Kathy Thomson	North of Britain
Monet [Waltz]	Graham & Avril Watkins	IDTA
Ocean	Kevin & Denise Jones	UKA
Weaver	Howard & Joanne Cookson	BATD
Wendy Jane	Don & June Millington	Butlins Skegness

Tangos (1999)

Bugibba [Tango] (O/T)	Neil & Leslie Marshall	BDC
Cherished (O/T)	Graham & Avril Watkins	Slough
Del-Mar [Tango] (O/T)	Darren Park & Andrea Kilgour	NCDTA
Regatta [Tango] (Mod)	Kevin Page & Valerie Laws	ISTD
Tasman (Mod)	Don & June Millington	Butlins Bognor Regis
Tropicana [Tango] (O/T)	Tracey Schofield & Alison Daley	ISDC
Zaraya [Tango] (O/T)	Andrew Pigg & Caroline Roberts	Blackpool

Saunters (1999)

Heather's	Dorothy Hudson & Ray Bulpitt	UKA
Mallory	Howard & Joan Cookson	BATD
Satinwood	Ian & Sue Webster	IDTA
Saunter for Elaine	Don & June Millington	NATD
Showboat	Jeff & Muriel Aldren	ADA
Tara's	Graham & Kathy Thomson	North of Britain

Foxtrots (1999)

Fernlea	Harry & Barbara Howarth	NCDTA
Irish Mist	Helen Blackburn & Steven Shaw	BDC
Laguna	Graham & Avril Watkins	ISDC
Monterey	Robert & Louise Aldred	Blackpool

Rumbas (1999)

Laburnum	Ian & Sue Webster	NCDTA
Makoré [Rumba]	Ian & Sue Webster	Butlins Bognor Regis
Morgan's	David & Margaret Cordell	BATD
Ravenglass	Michael & Angela Hayton	BDC
Twilight	Kevin & Denise Jones	Blackpool

Cha Cha Chas (1999)

Caborita	Ray & Bridget Fenton-Storey	Butlins Skegness
Larios	Neil & Lesley Marshall	SDTA
Madrid [Cha Cha]	Michael Morris & Beverley Berry	ADA
Monkey Puzzle	Ian & Sue Webster	ISTD
Quando	Kevin Page & Valerie Laws	NATD

Jives (1999)

Blue Jeans	Michael Morris & Beverley Berry	ISDC
Hot Spot	David & Dorothy Ainsworth	UKA
Jandia	Neil & Lesley Marshall	North of Britain
Jazzbox	Steven Shaw & Helen Blackburn	Slough

Quicksteps (1999)

Kahala	John & Maureen Dack	ADA
Khyber	Kevin Page & Valerie Laws	NATD
Quixote	Neil & Lesley Marshall	SDTA

Blues (1999)

Daniel	Graham & Avril Watkins	ISTD
White Heather	Graham & Kathy Thomson	SDTA

Miscellaneous

Dream Gavotte	John & Maureen Dack	Butlins Bognor Regis
Malibu Mambo	Steven Shaw & Helen Blackburn	IDTA
Sycamore Swing	Ian & Sue Webster	Butlins Skegness

Leading Arrangers 1999

5 – Ian & Sue Webster

4 – Neil & Leslie Marshall

4 – Don & June Millington

4 – Graham & Avril Watkins

3 – Kevin Page & Valerie Laws

3 – Steven Shaw & Helen Blackburn

3 – Graham & Kathy Thomson

2 – Howard & Joan Cookson

2 – John & Maureen Dack

2 – Kevin & Denise Jones

2 – Michael Morris & Beverley Berry

INDEX OF DANCES 1990 – 1999

Telecon (1992)
Tenacity (1997)
Terrifique (1995)
Thirlmere (1993)
Tigra (1995)
Tonite (1996)
Tony (1990)
Tornado (1992)
Torque (1991)
Torviscas (1992)
Totara (1996)
Trafalgar (1992)
Trent (1997)
Trésor (1996)
Trevini (1994)
Tripoli (1991)
Troodos (1993)
Tropicana (1999)
Turnberry (1993)
Tuscany (1991)
Vienna (1993)
Vilamoura (1990)
Yew Tree (1997)
Zaraya (1999)

Rumbas
Apollo (1993)
Atlanta (1992)
Caprice (1994)
Charlene (1990)
Continental (1995)
Cosmopolitan (1994)
Deargo (1995)
Delight (1990)
Dominique (1990)
Dorice (1994)
Eden Vale (1997)
Elise (1994)
Fantasia (1992)
Headlands (1994)
Invicta (1993)

Laburnum (1999)
Lakeside (1991)
Leon (1995)
Louise (1991)
Makoré (1999)
Marietta (1995)
Miami (1993)
Millennium (1998)
Miranda (1996)
Morgan's (1999)
Noir (1992)
Parisienne (1998)
Pineapple (1992)
Poldhu (1990)
Queen of Hearts (1997)
Quizas? (1995)
Radiant (1995)
Rafika (1992)
Raquel (1994)
Raspberry (1997)
Ravenglass (1999)
Raynham (1993)
Red Rose (1998)
Red Velvet (1998)
Redwood (1996)
Regency (1992)
Rembrant (1998)
Renaissance (1992)
Reno (1996)
Resolution (1998)
Richard's (1992)
Ritzy (1998)
Riverdale (1991)
Rosamar (1995)
Rosemount (1991)
Rosewood (1994)
Rossley (1997)
Rowan (1998)
Roxanne (1997)
Ruskin (1991)
Sabor (1990)

Samantha (1994)
Sapele (1996)
Tamara (1994)
Twilight (1999)
Venezia (1993)

Saunters
Azalia (1993)
Bel-Air (1990)
Carousel (1991)
Cedar (1997)
Centenary (1992)
Cerise (1992)
Columbine (1991)
Contara (1995)
Feline (1991)
Finesse (1998)
Heather's (1999)
Kingfisher (1990)
Kirsty (1990)
Mallory (1999)
Melrose (1993)
Navidia (1994)
Oxbury (1993)
Princess (1991)
Redrose (1991)
Romero (1993)
Salou (1996)
Samara (1990)
Sandalwood (1994)
Sandringham (1992)
Sateen (1991)
Satinwood (1999)
Saunter for Elaine (1999)
Saville (1998)
Seraya (1998)
Shakara (1992)
Sheldan (1998)
Shola (1995)
Showboat (1999)
Simplicity (1995)

Sinatra (1998)
Snowdrop (1997)
Solazur (1992)
Sonata (1994)
Sovereign (1994)
St. Clair (1992)
Strangward (1997)
Summer-Wind (1998)
Sunflower (1997)
Tara's (1999)
Valentine (1995)

Cha Cha Chas
Anitra (1991)
Beyzabanu (1997)
Caborita (1999)
Canasta (1998)
Capice (1998)
Carley (1990)
Caroland (1994)
Charlies (1993)
Chilli (1990)
Chinchilla (1990)
Christiana (1997)
CJ (1992)
Claymore (1991)
Clio (1991)
Cocobola (1998)
Colimar (1995)
Commador (1992)
Continental (1990)
Corrida (1990)
Cracker Barrel (1996)
Diamond Jubilee (1996)
D.J. (1996)
Dominion (1991)
Ebony (1992)
Empress (1996)
Issy (1998)
Kariokee (1995)

Katie (1993)
Larios (1999)
Madrid (1999)
Mahogany (1992)
Mario (1993)
Monkey Puzzle (1999)
Niki Noo (1995)
Par [Cha Cha] (1994)
Paradise (1994)
Quando (1999)
Rachel (1993)
Rosamar (1995)
Sarah's (1990)
Susie Q (1991)
Waikiki (1993)
Whiskey (1995)
Zanzibar (1997)

Foxtrots
Acacia (1995)
Albany (1998)
Amethyst (1996)
April (1992)
Cheslyn (1994)
Coniston (1998)
Derwent (1995)
Diamond Jubilee (1996)
Emerald (1994)
Ennerdale (1996)
Eternity (1997)
Fantasia (1995)
Felicity (1990)
Fernlea (1999)
Fortuna (1990)
Four Winds (1995)
Fragrance (1996)
Gardenia (1998)
Grosvenor (1991)
Harlequin (1990)
Irish Mist (1999)

Jasmine (1993)
Jessica 's (1998)
Laguna (1999)
Maple (1994)
Mirror Glass (1994)
Monterey (1999)
Nevada (1990)
Nicola (1991)
Passionata (1997)
Philishar (1993)
Sahara (1991)
Sea Breeze (1998)
Springtime (1997)
Stardust (1993)
Tempro (1992)
White Heather (1991)

Quicksteps
Appleby (1990)
Bernena (1994)
Carousel (1995)
Cassie (1996)
Chandella (1990)
Conomara (1998)
Coromandel (1996)
Cyprio (1995)
Elderberry (1998)
Florentine (1992)
Kahala (1999)
Kareen (1995)
Katrina (1992)
Katy (1993)
Kay's (1991)
Keaki (1998)
Kelly (1997)
Keresley (1997)
Khyber (1999)
Libra (1996)
Margie (1990)
Quality (1992)

Quatro (1991)
Queslett (1992)
Quintonian (1997)
Quixote (1999)
Richmond (1993)
Roxy (1991)
Somerset (1994)
Trojan (1994)

Jives

Alphabet (1990)
Bee Hive (1991)
Blackjack (1998)
Blue Jeans (1999)
Boogie Jive (1995)
Bucks Fizz (1996)
CK (1997)
Coca Rola (1994)
Cosmic (1996)
Disney (1991)
Gemma Lou (1996)
Honkeytonk (1997)
Hot Spot (1999)
Jackpot (1997)
Jambo (1993)
Jandia (1999)
Jazzbox (1999)
Jean's (1997)
Jennie (1994)
Jessica (1992)
Jetta (1990)
Jimpy (1991)
Joplin (1991)
Julie's (1993)
Jurassic (1993)
Kandy (1997)
Let's (1993)
Shelley (1990)

Swings

Abbey (1997)
Astral (1997)
Chevy (1993)
Gatsby (1996)
Gin (1998)
Ivory (1993)
Linden (1992)
Ryans (1995)
Sacha (1991)
Safron (1995)
Sandown (1991)
Savana (1990)
Shamrock (1994)
Sharron (1990)
Singapore (1992)
Sycamore (1999)
West (1996)

Blues

Aqua (1994)
Ballerina (1995)
Banyan (1996)
Berkeley (1990)
Bernstan (1995)
Bertie's (1995)
Boyden (1996)
Brandy (1998)
Cheney (1992)
Daniel (1999)
September (1998)
Stephanne (1993)
White Heather (1999)

Gavottes

Charlotte (1994)
Classical Grey (1997)
Dream (1999)
Emerald (1996)
Goiden (1997)
Golden Oak (1998)

Gwendoline (1990)
Lladro (1992)
Poirot (1995)
Primrose (1991)
Regency (1990)
Romany (1997)
Shimmering (1991)
Starlight (1993)
Sunset (1990)

Sambas

Marina (1990)
Miami (1994)
Popcorn (1991)
Scirocco (1993)
Sizzlers (1998)
Social (1992)
Susie (1995)

Bossa Novas

Bella (1992)
Blighty (1995)
Brazil (1996)

Mambas

Hey (1997)
Magic (1996)
Malibu (1999)
Mia (1997)
Mystique (1998)
Pain (1996)

Two Steps

Diamond Jubilee (1996)
Grenadier (1993)
Solara (1991)

Mazurka

Princess (1996)

Paso Doble

Paso Petite (1996)

NOTES